PUBLISHER/EDITOR
K. Allen Wood

CONTRIBUTING EDITORS
John Boden
Catherine Grant
Barry Lee Dejasu

COPY EDITOR
Sarah Gomes

LAYOUT/DESIGN
K. Allen Wood

COVER DESIGN
Mikio Murakami

Established in 2009
www.shocktotem.com

ISSN 1944-110X

Printed in the United States of America.

Notes from the Editor's Desk

Welcome to issue #10!

I'm sad to say it's been a while. Even sadder to say it might be a while longer before we find ourselves here again.

Here's why.

In the past two issues I discussed how life had changed after the birth of my son, how finding the time to do even the simplest tasks had become increasingly difficult if not impossible. Well, my wife and I now have two kids. Our son is halfway to three years old, and our daughter just turned one.

(If you have children, you're probably nodding along right now, knowing where this is going.)

She arrived early, so this issue—which was originally scheduled for a January 2015 release, then July 2015—arrived late. *Very* late.

As some of you may know, I work from home. It's a great job. But that means I'm also a stay-at-home dad (also a great job). That's two full-time jobs. Add to that writing, editing, publishing, and countless other everyday things, and to say my plate is full would be a dizzying understatement.

And editing *Shock Totem* has never been an easy task. From the beginning it's always been a lot of work and a lot money. Even without kids, each issue was a hell of an undertaking (and being something of a perfectionist certainly doesn't help).

So where does that leave us?

Well, the easy answer is: this is the final issue of *Shock Totem*. Boom! Done. Ten regular issues, three holiday issues. Thirteen total. A fitting number, right?

Yeah, but we're not done. I'm bullheaded. I don't like easy. You see, I have not lost the desire to publish the magazine; I've lost the time. And I stubbornly hold onto the hope that I can either find the time or find some other way to put out more issues. Maybe bring on a new editor or something like that. It's worth exploring, that's for sure.

So no, this is not the end of *Shock Totem*. Not yet. However, there will be a necessary intermission, a hiatus. Hopefully brief—*ish*.

Now, to be clear, when I say *Shock Totem*, I am strictly speaking of the magazine. Shock Totem Publications is alive and well, and we are still moving forward into the book market (editing a novel or novella is infinitely easier than editing a magazine). We have three fantastic novellas and one collection slated for release this year, and if time permits a few other things. Stick around for a while, will you?

And so that brings us to this, issue #10. A long time coming, but worth the wait, I think.

Before parting, I'd like to thank each author for being so graciously patient during this long process. I am truly grateful that you stuck with me. Because your contributions—and the contributions of all those who came before you—are truly what makes *Shock Totem* great. I am just the messenger.

So please enjoy this one, folks, and hopefully we meet here again someday soon.

K. Allen Wood
February 19, 2016

Contents

Article
RUMOR AND SHADOW: THE HAUNTING OF THE EVERETT MANSION

by Barry Lee Dejasu

I went to college at a haunted house. At least, that's the best way to describe the main building of Southern Vermont College in Bennington, VT. Built in 1922 by a local beer baron named Edward Everett, the building is a sprawling stone mansion set high on a hill, with a huge courtyard and a mountainside cascade of fountains. Inside, the mansion is festooned with windows facing in on long hallways, lofty rooms, and arched ceilings. By day, the Edward Everett Mansion is utterly beautiful; but at night, it hardly takes a ghost story to cast an eerie light on it.

Motion-activated floodlights, set on certain corners of the building, only shed enough light to promise safe passage for a short distance, and the shadows are thick enough to appear solid. An adjoining garage building features an old, rusted metal trapdoor on one wall, once used for delivering firewood; when the metal door is lifted open, its rusty creaks filling the air, the darkness beyond is so absolute that only a terrible face jumping out of the shadows beyond could break the solid black. The courtyard is closed in by the side of the mansion, as well as by walls that separate the forest from its stone grounds, which are laid out like a massive, celestial wheel. Up the mountainside cascade and into the forest, further structures can be found, including an old, wide, flat stone table, upon which many an imagination has been laid, in bloody sacrifice, to rumor.

At night, the interior of the mansion is all but perfectly silent and still. Security guards patrolling the hallways might occasionally pause to listen to a phantom creak; perhaps students, trespassing the mansion to play sardines or even looking for ghosts, are lurking about—but such attempts at stealth can only go so far, and the guards have to suppress a shiver and move on. Up the twisting stairways and onto the second floor, where the darkened rooms, once living quarters for guests and servants alike, are often left open at night, their desks and tables half-visible in the ambient floodlights from outside. On the third floor, the hallways are far narrower, the windows to the offices much smaller, and the shadows more pronounced. A wide, circular room, its ceiling marked by four crossed beams, is the source of much debate—namely, that the hook at the center of those beams was once where a noose had been hung for a doomed soul. And in the basement, a narrow passage has been turned into a darkroom for aspiring photographers, with a sign hung on the door that says KEEP THE DOOR CLOSED, OR THE DARK COMES OUT.

But none of this is to say that the mansion is really *haunted*. That's just the popular association one makes with such a huge, old building. Not to mention,

Bennington was a very spooky place in the 1940's, when several people went missing in the woods near Glastonbury Mountain; since then, the area has often been referred to as the "Bennington Triangle." And of course the author Shirley Jackson had lived in Bennington for many years, and wrote her classic novel *The Haunting of Hill House* there. So of *course* the big, spooky mansion is a host for much speculation of supernatural terrors.

In 2000, I began attending SVC as a bright-eyed, bushy-tailed freshman. The night of my orientation included a "ghost walk," during which fellow students and I were led up the steep hill, through the woods, and into the mansion, where spooky stories were shared and a few attempts at scares were performed. It was all in good fun, of course, and nobody saw anything; but our appetites had been whetted. We wanted to believe in the mansion's haunted reputation. We wanted to see ghosts. We wanted to be *scared*.

Every now and then, groups of friends might take nocturnal walks from the dorms at the base of the hill to explore the mansion's grounds. The lawn has a beautiful view of the starry dome above, and benches set beside a path through the woods have an excellent view of the valley below and the mountains beyond. The woods are deep and dark, and occasionally host an unpermitted bonfire. But not all who visit the mansion at night are seeking beauty or retreat; many are seeking the sensation of *fear*.

I remember one night going for such a walk with a few friends. Matt, Rickie, and myself either believed, or very much *wanted* to believe, in what we were headed up to see, whereas Jason was particularly vocal about his skepticism. We patrolled the grounds for at least half an hour, but for the most part, we saw nothing. At one point, we felt a collective chill as we thought we saw a shadowy figure moving before one of the windows, but similar glimpses in other windows led to the realization that they were in fact just curtains gently swaying with the evening breeze.

We ended up in the courtyard, frustrated and bored, and the others decided it was time to go back to the dorms. In my disappointment, I stopped and insisted that we take one last spin around the building. Though reluctant, everyone agreed to go.

On the lawn side of the building, two of the windows were open: one from a second-floor office; the other from the third floor's circular room. Not one of us questioned whether they had already been open when we'd first visited that side of the building; *they had been most definitely closed*, yet here they were, little winks in the building's face. Nor had it been the doing of security guards; they had not yet come by for their hourly inspections—in fact, they only just pulled up into the parking lot as we were leaving later. All of us were quite spooked by this; Jason had trouble explaining what he was seeing. We never did find out just how those windows had opened, and I don't think any of us ever really *wanted* to know.

I wish I could say that all of the mansion's creepier moments came from such intentional excursions, but fear has no such discretion. In my last two years at the college, I worked the closing shift at the library, an enormous, beautiful wood-paneled room on the mansion's first floor that was once a grand dining room, its massive chandeliers still hanging resplendently from the ceiling. I would sit at a desk by the library's front entrance, welcoming people as they came and went, and helping search for books as needed. At the end of my shift, I had to make sure that any stray books were put away, all computers were powered down, close the offices and the quiet room, lock the doors, shut off the lights, and leave. I learned early on the proper way to go about this, for one night, I shut off the lights as I went through each room, from the front desk onward, so that by the time I reached the quiet room and closed the doors, I had trapped myself at the end of an entire passage of almost perfect darkness, with no flashlight or any other means to make the trip any less ominous. I never really encountered anything in the library, but it was sensationally creepy at night; and this is not to mention the entire walk I had to take down the hill, be it by the curving, half-lit street or by the hill's grassy incline, before I was back in the safe and sane light of the dorms.

One's nose might on occasion catch a whiff of phantom odors inside the mansion or upon its grounds; rumors state that the smell of lilac blossoms can be detected in the presence of certain restless spirits. Although I had spent most of my years at the college not encountering any such odor, I had numerous occasions of enjoying the sweet fragrance of unseen flowers on my walks up and down the road to the mansion. One summer, while traveling with my parents, I detected that particular smell, and asked my mother what it was; of course, she revealed that smell to be lilac, and to this day, I can't smell it and get quite the same joy anymore, not without a slight accompanying chill.

And although since discontinued due to a new fire policy, the mansion used to be a tourist destination every Halloween. Near the end of every October, from my freshman year onward, I helped a group of students and faculty set up the mansion for two weekend nights. We would decorate certain rooms for the event, filling them with dead leaves, skeletons, mazes of wooden frames and black fabric, strobe lights, and of course lots of spooky music. Groups of people would be toured through the mansion, one room after another, with our participants jumping forth from the shadows to scare the living daylights out of the visitors. It was in my senior year's Haunted Mansion event that I learned a valuable lesson in scaring for fun: it is often a double-edged sword.

The tours that year were being led around the outside of the mansion in the dark, where they were accosted by various terrors before going inside. They went up a twisted stairway and straight into a leaf-filled room on the second floor. After the horrors of that room, they were led out onto a balcony that connected it to a neighboring room. There, murderous figures chased the group out and past an adjoining, darkened hallway, where a half-glimpsed phantom came sweeping and howling out of the shadows, chasing them further into the halls of the haunted mansion.

I was that hallway-phantom; wearing all black clothing, a black hood and cloak, and a black mask, I would stand in front of a tall, darkly-varnished door at the far end of the hallway and wait for the group to enter the first room. Then I would move to the middle of the hallway and wait for them to re-emerge before silently running to them, screaming. At one point, I even worked with my roommate at the time by having him pretend to be part of one of the tour groups before grabbing him and taking him into the shadows.

It was during one of my waits for a new group to arrive that something strange happened. I was standing before the door at the end of the hall as usual; the room beyond the door was being used to store the desks that had been moved out of the other rooms, and its door was held shut on pneumatic hinges, so one would have to push on it in order to enter. There I stood before the door, not touching it, when I heard it *thump shut behind me.* Nearly jumping right out of my cloak, I spun to the door and nervously called out to my prankster that he or she was very funny; but when I heard neither laughter nor response, I pushed the door open and peeked in. It was almost perfectly pitch-black inside, and the murky light from the hall lent a few reflections to the metallic legs on the stacked desks and chairs inside. I stood there, staring into the dark room, wondering how on earth the door could have been open, and all the more disquieted by another thought: *how long* had I stood there, my back turned to that void? A moment later, I told a couple of my fellow participants that I would be moving my post elsewhere.

Whether or not the mansion is haunted by spirits, I don't think anybody will ever truly know; but the power of belief in the unknown is as mysterious and powerful as it is old, and it's easy for one to believe in one's eyes when they catch a glimpse of something lurking in the darkened hallways of the Everett Mansion.

The Henson Curse

by Paul A. Hamilton

Bargaining: October 9, 2018, 5:53 PM

Had there been any way to guess, I would have made Junjun sweeter-looking. Not for her benefit necessarily, although I knew her well enough to read the cues: she hated the way she looked. Beyond the inherent oddity of being Awakened, people cast judgment because of her appearance. She hated it and hid it as best she could with long sleeves and a drawn-up hood. Even I struggled to really look at her, to take her in and see her for everything that she was. The bulbous yellow eyes stared back at me, lids sliding over them, the pupils I had dabbed on with a tiny pip of black paint now dilated and radiating insistence.

"There has to be another way," I said.

"No," she replied with my own voice, slightly higher and much softer.

I waited the three seconds, the way we had practiced over the years. Sharing vocal cords can actually be painful if you try to talk over yourself. Self-preservation is, after all, the mother of compromise.

"We can find another therapist," I offered.

"No more therapists. You can't afford it, and I can't take another lecture on positive thinking." Junjun folded her arms across her tiny chest, the mauve fur there rustling in the breeze of my desk fan.

"Let's at least have dinner," I suggested. "We'll talk about it some more."

"Zack," she said, still gentle but exasperated, "we've talked enough."

When it was clear she wasn't going to follow that thought with anything, I snorted. I caught a glimpse of myself in the mirror over the mantel. In a way it hadn't for years, the absurdity of it shook me. The involuntary spray of a disbelieving laugh had to be covered with a cough. One thought took center stage in my mind: *there's a crazy bastard, arguing with his hand.*

"It's just dinner, okay?" I said. "Come on, I'll buy you some oranges."

She stared over her hooked beak for a long beat, then punished me with one of her smiles. I hadn't designed her to be capable of pleasant expressions, so her smile always came across as a sinister leer.

"Deal," she said. "Don't forget to stop by the closet so I can get my hoodie."

Anger: October 9, 2018, 6:12 PM

I guess the boy meant well. By that point, I was just so sensitive to the stares and the attention, which was ironic or funny for someone used to living life on a stage. The thing about being a puppeteer, though: it's all about hiding from the direct spotlight. Living for the attention and the applause and the appreciation, sure, but unlike actors or dancers or singers, puppeteers filter that through their creation. They let the proxy take the bow, and every victory is an illusion.

"Is he, you know, real?" The boy was young, seven or eight at most, right about the target age for my shows. Before the Awakening, that is. He had stalked me into the produce section of the grocery store, creeping closer while I inspected the overpriced and imported fruit.

The gender assumption of the question irritated me. I guess I never did determine Junjun's gender—if Awakened even have genders. When I was building her out of foam and Antron Fleece in my workshop, I had thought of her as female. She never complained, so I kept assuming.

"It's a she," I said.

"So she's alive," the boy corrected himself quickly.

"Yes."

"Did it hurt?"

"Yes, it fucking hurt," I growled. It was a lie, or most of one. The sudden fuse of material to flesh, the rend of bone and sharp downward pull of tissue coagulating into new forms at the end of my arm—I might have expected some physical agony from a transformation like that. But it was instantaneous, painless. The real torment came from the cleave in my mind of abruptly having a living thing attached to the end of my arm. Of accepting it.

The boy nodded, as if this was the answer he expected. I rolled my eyes, anticipating the next question.

"How did it happen?"

I sighed. "Get lost, kid."

He forged on. "My friend Billy Zuicker says some old puppeteer cursed all the puppets in the whole world."

Some old puppeteer. Kids today.

"Sure, I've heard that, too." I acted disinterested, hoping to end the conversation, while also looking around for the kid's parents. He should know better than to talk to strangers.

"Billy says it happened twenty-five years after that guy's death." He leaned in conspiratorially. "To the minute," he stage whispered.

"Billy watches too much TV," I said, still trying to identify a responsible adult among the other shoppers milling around the produce section. Although, Billy Zuicker wasn't wrong about the coincidental timing of the Awakening.

"Can I touch her?"

It was, in retrospect, an innocent enough request. Certainly the kind of thing that I would have smiled at and happily indulged prior to the Awakening. I'm sure it was just the timing of the thing, the conversation with Junjun, the tumor of knowledge of what I was being asked to do pressing against the back of my mind. Whatever the case, I just lost it.

"Well, I don't know. Maybe you could introduce yourself to her." I felt my remaining hand tremble and Junjun began glancing around, alarmed at the scene

SHOCK TOTEM | THE HENSON CURSE

I was about to make. "Offer to shake her hand. Use some goddamn manners, maybe? She's not a pet, you little shit, she's a person." Technically speaking, at the time, the United States Supreme Court had not conclusively ruled this to be true. The kid's brown eyes widened and his lip slid out like a cash drawer. The anger mixed with familiar fear as I looked up and saw a furious man with a striking resemblance to the child standing behind him.

The worst part is, I had no real issue with the kid. In fact, any other day, any other time, it would have been a wonderful opportunity. Junjun was good with kids, she always had been. In spite of her self-consciousness and villainous exterior, when approached by a child too innocent to prejudge her, she typically thrived. Too late, she measured up the scenario with the boy's father and tried to diffuse it.

"Hey," she said, quietly even for her, "it's okay. I'll shake your hand."

"The hell you will," the dad thundered, wrapping a pudgy, protective hand across the boy's chest. He was yelling at me, even though he was replying to Junjun.

"Okay, I'm sorry," Junjun said, withdrawing immediately, retreating into the simpering, timid wretch I had grown accustomed to. My own fury hid behind self-preservation and the curtain I kept between myself and the world.

I wish I could say that closed-off existence coincided with Junjun's Awakening.

Shock: May 16, 2015, 5:14 AM

James Maury Henson passed away in a New York City hospital from a freak bout of pneumonia. Exactly twenty-five years later I was in my workshop. I had no reason to be there. My wife was upstairs in bed. Junjun, who would be the villain in my new comedic fantasy production, was more or less complete. Back then, my life was a series of minor discomforts and inconveniences: asthma, insomnia, eczema, tennis elbow, carpal tunnel syndrome, allergies, repetitive stress injuries, scoliosis, hemorrhoids. None of it acute enough to warrant concern. All of it severe enough to keep me in a state of low level misery.

My puppeteer friends would, of course, make a note of the Henson anniversary. Not as much as they did on September 24th, his birthday, but it wouldn't go unnoticed in that crowd. Toasts and viewing parties of favorite Muppet episodes would abound. To me, though, Henson was a populist. A kiddie crowd pleaser. His work was educational, common denominational, vanilla. Anyone could make cute characters and give them chipper counting-and-alphabet personalities. Sure, his work in films—the stuff with the darker edge—was great, but I tried to keep a level head about it. No one is above criticism.

My wife, Sandy, pushed open the door and scrubbed the back of her hand over her eyes. "Trouble sleeping?"

"Yeah. I'll be up in a bit." I had Junjun on my arm, testing the blinking mechanism and the articulation points. Sandy gave Junjun a sour look.

"He's ugly," she said.

"Well, she's a bad guy, so..." Sandy's face was exasperation and exhaustion and utter disinterest. Not feigned indifference like you might give to someone you indulge because you love, but contemptuous apathy.

"Try not to stay up too long. We have to do the shopping."

"Okay," I said. "'Night."

Sandy shook her head and pulled the door closed.

Thirty seconds later, someone screamed with my voice and I tried to scream, too. I remember a tingle. I remember looking into those huge, yellow eyes and seeing life there. Real life; a level of realism that could not be faked with my meager skills. Junjun didn't just blink and move from my commands, she recoiled from me, looked down at the connection point between us. Where there had been a draped cuff of fabric, now there was a mat of purplish fur disappearing into a seam of flesh, red and puffy like a fresh wound, recently stitched. The rod that allowed me to manipulate her small hands was pulled from my grasp as her articulating fingers scrabbled at her front.

If you have a strong stomach, you can look up some of the stories and even a couple of videos—mostly from European countries where the hour wasn't quite so ungodly and actual puppet shows were taking place—from that moment. People say when weird things happen they fall into denial, believe themselves to be dreaming, or that they stop processing memories. The experience for me was like being hit by a virus as big as a truck. My body rebelled and I fell over, Junjun trying in vain to catch something out of self-preservation, my muscles beset instantly with a deep ache. My temperature regulation went sideways, and I began to shiver and sweat in unison. My throat erupted in slicing pain like razorwire was being drawn through it while Junjun and I continued to grunt and scream with the same set of vocal cords.

Junjun tried to right herself first, the sensation of her autonomous movement like holding an angry cat in a carrier—the yank of weight and shifting gravity and foreign will I could only just control. Her arm, the one connected to the control rod, whipped up, and the rod slapped me in the face. I cursed and she cowered. The door opened and Sandy looked down on us as we turned toward her in unison.

"What is all the racket about?"

"What's happening to me?" Junjun said.

"Something's wrong," I croaked.

Sandy rolled her eyes. "Oh, for the love of God, Zachary. Get off the floor. I thought you were actually hurt."

"Who is she?" Junjun said, frantic. "Where am I?"

The glare Sandy gave me when she thought I was fooling around with my puppet held the regret of six years stemming from a single bad decision. She'd said yes, she'd meant no, and this was the result.

"Get up," she said.

"Call an ambulance," I said.

"Get him off me!"

Sandy took four steps toward me, reached out and grabbed Junjun's head, meaning to yank the puppet off my arm, to fling it away from me. Her fury made her blind to the subtle differences in Junjun, to the real suffering that was crippling me.

Junjun screamed when Sandy pulled. Junjun flailed against the assault, movements a puppet wasn't capable of. I saw panic, disbelief, and incomprehension fill the space on Sandy's face where rage had been. Her grip didn't falter until Junjun opened her maw. The cavity there was not a blackened illusion, but the wet glisten of a real tongue and the gleam of genuine teeth. Junjun bit down on Sandy's arm. I'm sure it was instinctive self-defense, nothing more.

The howls of pain and revulsion, the screech of lunatic disbelief and the vile filth directed at Junjun would set the stage for all the other welcomes she would ever receive. I shivered on the floor, holding my foreign arm as far from me as I could, exposing Junjun to Sandy's verbal assault, while I tried not to let my mind disintegrate.

Denial: October 9, 2018, 6:18 PM

I fled the grocery store, leaving my basket of items behind, ducking under a hail of threats from the over-protective but under-attentive father. Junjun buried her face in my armpit and clutched my chest with her arms, shaking and sobbing in her surreal, transferred way. I fumed, each step teetering on the edge of an about-face that would allow me to confront the man, to reclaim some dignity and show Junjun how things could be different. By the time I had made the decision to go back, I was halfway home.

The tiny convenience store on the corner by my house is one of the few places I go with any regularity. It forces me into a steady diet of processed nutrition bars and canned beef stew, but I know Oskar, the guy who owns the place. I'm safe there.

Outside the store, Holly scrabbled to her feet when she saw us approaching. "Junjun!" she cried, clapping her ink-stained hands.

Holly was a street artist, one of those intentionally nomadic people rotating between friends' couches, shelters, tent cities, and the occasional stoop with a generous awning. She had a tie-dyed bandana over her hair, hiding either an unfortunate attempt at dreadlocks or just a chronic lack of shampoo.

Junjun pulled the edge of her hood back with a trembling hand. "Hi, Holly," she said, so softly I doubted Holly could hear.

"How's my favorite purple people-eater?" Holly's inflection was common with people addressing shy children or the mentally disabled.

"Okay, I guess," Junjun lied.

"It's a little hot to be wearing the hood, isn't it?"

"Not for me."

I shifted my stance, hoping a friendly face might make headway with Junjun where my meager arguments could not.

"Hey! I got something for you!" Holly turned and fetched a grimy knapsack from her panhandling station and rummaged around, the tip of her tongue poking through chapped lips. Junjun's curiosity must have let her forget the scene with the boy's father for a moment. She drew back her hood and clutched her small hands to her middle, leaning over to get a glimpse inside Holly's pack. She picked at the nub on her left wrist where she had clipped off the control rod like an oversized fingernail.

"Here!" Holly said, whipping out a rumpled piece of black construction paper. She presented it to Junjun with a wide smile that might have been beautiful if not for the sick, brownish teeth.

Junjun accepted the paper with slow, cautious movements and turned it over, revealing a competent chalk sketch depicting a public bath filled with naked women, most washing their hair. On the left ledge, an old crone with drooping breasts was being coaxed into the water. Later, I learned it was a reproduction of a mid-16th century painting by a guy named Cranach. It was called *The Fountain of Youth*. Holly's white-on-black reproduction looked a bit like a photo negative. I liked Holly's version better.

"I love it," Junjun said, clutching it. "Thank you, Holly."

"You're welcome."

"Thank you," I reiterated, trying to ignore the look of confusion on Holly's face, as if I had just repeated myself. I moved toward the door, thinking I would have to give her my change.

Holly walked backward toward her little nest. To Junjun, she said, "I wish I could take you home with me."

We were inside the store and out of earshot before Junjun replied, "No, you don't," under our breath.

When I saw that it wasn't Oskar behind the counter, I should have just turned around, gone home, stalled for time. The man perched at the register had a sloppy beard and a hard stare. Junjun instinctively withdrew into her hood and tucked Holly's drawing into her front pocket. Oskar kept a small basket near the counter filled with brown bananas and greenish, flavorless oranges, usually patrolled by a few well-rewarded fruit flies. I told myself it would be fine, that the earlier incident was a fluke that was becoming less common.

I selected two of the least withered-looking fruits out of the display, depositing them on the counter. I forced myself to meet the unfamiliar man's cold stare with a defiant silence. He stood unmoving and unblinking for a dozen hammered heartbeats. I sniffled. "Just these, please."

He folded his arms across his chest. He wasn't big or intimidating, though he had a couple of inches on me. It was the nothingness behind his gaze that made my mouth go dry. He made no move toward the register.

"Hello? Can I buy these?"

"No," he said. The word was final, flat and heavy like a stone.

"You won't sell me these oranges," I said, as if the concept were absurd.

The man just stood there, staring at me.

"I'm a paying customer, you know."

His eyes moved up to the television mounted over the soda aisle, the indication clear that he was done with me.

"Hey, you! Pay attention here! You're a store clerk. All you do is take money in exchange for the items on sale. Do your goddamn job!"

"Let's go, let's just go," Junjun whispered in that soft, inaudible way she did when she wanted to communicate with me without being overheard. I actually hated when she did that, hated the spidery way it tickled my throat, the self-consciousness it gave me of being caught singing alone in the car. I'm not sure if it was the cashier's attitude or Junjun using her secret whisper that prompted me to do what I did next.

I snatched one of the oranges off the counter, not trusting myself to palm them both at once, and curled a lip at the attendant. "You won't sell it to me? Then fuck you, I'll just take it." I walked out. I didn't look back, although I think the guy chased me at least to the front door. There must have been an internal debate about leaving the shop unattended to continue his pursuit, because he shouted insults from the doorway and then turned his ire on Holly. The whole time Junjun was clawing for the orange and begging me to bring it back, to forget it, it wasn't worth the trouble. I ignored her, stuffed it in my pocket out of her reach and marched home.

Reflection: August 19th, 2019, 10:55 AM

"What was your state of mind when you left Neighbor-Mart that evening, Mr. Lindgren?" The Assistant District Attorney was a stony-faced woman named Trudy Pickney.

"I was angry. I was very upset."

"Were you angry at the attendant?"

"Yes, naturally." I wore a suit my lawyer bought for me. It was foreign-made and cheap and it itched, but he instructed me not to fidget as it makes witnesses look dishonest. So instead I sweated against the discomforts I usually dealt with and the new one brought on by the suit and I ended up looking dishonest anyway.

"But you couldn't confront Mr. Kasival, could you?" Pickney's slim hands rested in a practiced grip on the edge of the podium. When she spoke she leaned a little into the microphone, which made her Bs and Ps pop. For all her poise, this one persistent flaw struck me as sloppy and unprofessional.

"I don't understand the question."

"You were enraged, as you stated. Would you say you wanted an outlet? A place to channel your anger?"

"Objection," my lawyer said.

"Overruled."

I ran my tongue around the inside of my cheeks, and drew a glare from the lawyer.

"I'm used to dealing with frustration," I said.

"Dealing with it?" Pickney said in a way that made me think of a pounce. "Or repressing it?"

My lawyer told me they'd play the bottled-up loner angle.

"Dealing with it." I was firm about that.

"And what about Junjun? How did she deal with it?"

"You'd have to ask her," I sneered, drawing an uncomfortable murmur from the crowd. Pickney made a face, forged ahead.

"You characterized her as 'somewhat withdrawn, difficult to read,' didn't you?"

"You have the transcript," I said, shrugging.

"Watch it, Mr. Lindgren," the judge said. She was stern and obviously frustrated by the media attention of the trial, but she had a dark sense of humor and I found myself liking her very much.

"Okay, sure. I said that."

"How much did you try to get to know Junjun, Mr. Lindgren?" Pickney asked.

A fine question, in fact. Did I ever really try with Junjun? What was Junjun to me? A possessed hand? A parasite? I could have made our shared existence easier, I suppose, if I had been more open to the symbiosis. But all I knew of relationships was barriers: the walls between me and my audiences, the secrets between me and my lovers, the silences between me and everyone else. How much can you learn about the personality of a living, self-aware puppet? They didn't have the personas their creators projected onto them before the Awakening. Junjun, designed to be a cruel villain, was sweet-tempered and painfully introverted. Elmo, on the other hand, turned out to be a class-A asshole. There was no more creator input once they sprang to life.

"As much as you try to get to know anything that shares a body with you," I said.

Pain: October 9, 2018, 9:01 PM

She wouldn't eat the orange. Her position didn't change. I tried to talk her out of it, but I don't think I was terribly convincing. Some part of me, a deep and secret part I jail with my ribs and cover with lies, cheered her on. It didn't want me to win the debate and it longed for her to settle on the trump card: "This is happening, with you or without you." We never got there. I ran out of things to say.

I went back to my workshop. It seemed fitting to have it end where it began. The room hadn't been used in years. Why would it? No one needed puppets; no one even put them on anymore. There hadn't been any more occurrences of them coming to life, but no one dared take the chance.

I spread clear plastic sheeting over the workshop carpet, and draped everything else in old painter's cloths. I fretted about the walls, but couldn't think of what else to do about them that didn't require a trip to the store.

There was no hurry in it, and Junjun kept a cool zen as I made a special trip to the kitchen, retrieved the cordless phone and dialed 911, but didn't press Send. Another trip to the bathroom and I returned with a bit of elastic tape, the kind Sandy used to use when her knees swelled up. The tourniquet took some coordinated effort between Junjun and I to apply. Physiologically, enough was known about the Awakened for certain specialists to treat them, but I wasn't a doctor. I was just an out of work children's entertainer, fumbling my way through a violent emancipation. I held an end of the tape in my teeth while the stub of my arm buzzed and I saw Junjun's complexion go ashen and her eyes get milky.

As I fiddled with the chop saw, trying to get the angle just right so it could drop smoothly and cut clean and fast, Junjun closed her eyes and folded her claw-like hands over Holly's picture, as if in prayer.

"Last chance," I said to her.

She didn't reply. Instead she gave me that queer grimace that passed for a smile, and a tiny little nod.

Reconstruction: August 20th, 2019, 1:12 PM

"They said she didn't suffer."

"That mattered to you?" My lawyer, one Pierre Underwood, lacked the confident air that Pickney carried in spades. He was weaselly, and despite his insistence that I not fidget, he couldn't seem to remain still.

"Sure, of course."

"Did you know what severing Junjun from your arm would do?"

"Basically, yeah. I guess."

"Can you elaborate on that?" Underwood said.

"I don't know. I think... I kind of hoped she'd be okay. Maybe. You know? Like that wasn't just going to be...it. For her."

"You thought she might have a chance."

"Yeah. Maybe."

"Do you think Junjun knew what the amputation would do?"

"Objection," Pickney chimed in.

"Sustained."

"Okay," Underwood said, "how about this: did Junjun ever tell you she wanted to die?"

"We talked about it. Sort of. She never framed it that way, though. To her, it was about freedom. It was a gift she was giving me." Unconsciously, I scratched at the stump left of my arm, just slightly more than an elbow's worth. "She wanted us to be apart, that's how she put it."

"To her, freedom meant dying?"

"Objection," Pickney said.

"Overruled," the judge said, but her tone indicated Underwood and I needed to be careful.

"She never said as much, but..." I looked at the judge. She seemed interested to hear the end of the thought. "I'm fairly certain she thought death was her escape."

"Objection."

"Enough already, Ms. Pickney. We get it," the judge said. "Mr. Underwood, can we move on?"

Pickney glared.

There was only one part of the plan Junjun and I never discussed. It was this, the aftermath. We debated the hows and the whys and the what-ifs, the shoulds, cans, what-other-options-do-we-haves. But we didn't discuss what would be left.

"Mr. Lindgren, you're being charged with murder. Let me ask you. Do you think what you did constitutes a murder?" Underwood had prepped me for the question, but as I heard it come out of his mouth, it had a fresh resonance. Like a song you've heard a thousand times and that one thousand and first listen reveals a guitar flourish or a lyric you hadn't noticed before. Was I a murderer? The question was designed to let me say my piece about what Awakened were: an extraordinary phenomenon, but one that ultimately was parasitic, reliant on the host, incapable of independent life. It was to set the stage for expert witnesses, psychologists and biologists who would testify that what I had done was more like pulling off a leech than killing a human.

But I sat there beneath the glares of hundreds of people and millions more on screens around the world, more exposed now than ever before. What did we leave behind? A criminal? A cold corpse? A savior or a murderer? Was all that remained a lonely, remorseful man?

It was all of those things.

I leaned into the mic. "I don't know," I said. "I just know it was mercy."

Acceptance: November 1st, 2019, 4:10 PM

The TV aired my special again. I hated it, but couldn't drag my eyes from it. I watched TV in the room that used to be my workshop. It's sort of a den now. Maybe shrine is a better word.

"Who is Zachary Lindgren?" The deep-voiced announcer asked.

Who indeed. I saw the flash of a hundred thousand flashbulbs strobe around my face, the discomfort etched beneath the surface of eyes as dead as a lifeless puppet's. In the end, it was always me that was under control. I wish I'd seen that earlier. I thought about how I'd answer the announcer's question if anyone bothered trying to get my side of the story anymore.

Who am I?

This: a puppeteer. Someone feigning life for attention. A professional manipulator.

Just some crazy bastard arguing with his invisible hand.

Paul Hamilton is a writer and technology worker living in Northern California with his wife and two daughters. His stories feature broken people, reassembled worlds, beautiful monsters, and hideous love. He gets his inspiration by impersonating an old-timey bartender, listening to stories told by lonely strangers. When not writing, he can be found reading, drawing, taking photographs, or riding roller coasters. More from him can be found at www.ironsoap.com, and on Twitter as @ironsoap.

Blue John

by D.K. Wayrd

I'm behind the bar shucking oysters when Blue John enters the tavern. He's wearing a plain tweed suit instead of a policeman's uniform, but still moves with a constable's swagger. "Boy," he says, "where's your master?" I lay down my knife and leave to find Father, to tell him our new lodger has arrived.

That night, in the storeroom where I sleep, I drag my straw pallet to a spot over Blue John's cellar room. Gaps between the floorboards give me a slivered view: a table, a wardrobe, a bed. Blue John sits half-naked at the table, his bull-chest covered with dark curly hair. He holds a red leather journal in his lap and strokes it lightly, as though petting a cat, before opening it and beginning to write. The rest of the cavernous room is dark, beyond the reach of the gas lamp.

~

"Finch, go to Blue John," Father says the next morning. "He needs help."

The cellar stairs are in the back courtyard, between pig sty and privy. Blue John's door is open, and I see a policeman's coat and helmet hanging from pegs on the wall. The coat still has its silver buttons; the helmet shows only a stain where the starburst shield of the Metropolitan Police once gleamed.

I hear the screech of nails ripping from wood. Blue John stands over a packing crate, pry bar in hand. Inside the crate is a slant-topped work desk with many drawers, each drawer only a few inches high. We wrestle the desk to the center of the room and place it next to the iron frame of a machine. Other boxes yield a metal disc larger than a dinner plate, long cylinders covered in india-rubber, an iron wheel like that of a small steam engine. I hold and fetch and carry while Blue John builds. The iron skeleton becomes a letterpress, a one-man machine operated by a foot treadle.

Blue John pauses to wipe his oily hands and looks me up and down. "You don't say much, do you?"

I shake my head.

"Speak up."

"Yes, sir."

"Louder. I want to hear you yell."

"Yell what?"

Blue John grins. "Yell–*Shocking Murder!*"

"Shocking murder," I say, and Blue John's arm lashes out. My elbow explodes with pain. "*Bloody hell,*" I shout.

"That's better," Blue John says. A leather-covered blackjack dangles from his hand. "You've got to make noise to get anywhere in this world. Try again."

I haven't raised my voice since the cholera took Mother, since Father turned into a silent grey husk. I close my eyes and take a great breath, then shout with all my might.

"I suppose you'll do," Blue John says. "I'll arrange it with your father."

~

That night in the tavern I ask Father what Blue John wants. "Later," Father says, and sets me to clearing dishes and wiping down cutlery. When his back is turned I steal away to sit with Nettie and Alva at their usual corner table, where Nettie is reading aloud from the *London Almanack*. "September's full moon is called the harvest moon," she says, her voice clear despite her many missing teeth.

"Should be called the harlot's moon," Alva says. "Enough light to show off the goods, without showing the bad." They laugh, though I can't imagine Alva having any bad bits.

I slide onto the bench next to Nettie, who is old and no longer on the game. Retired, she says, living off her savings and day-work at a coffee house. Nettie enjoys cosseting me and starts combing out my curly hair with her fingers. "Pretty enough to be a girl," she says, "but be thankful you're a boy." Alva pulls a red ribbon from her dark hair and tries to drape it round my head. I jerk away, unnerved by the touch of her hand on my cheek.

"The new lodger," I say, "why is he called Blue John?"

Nettie argues it is because he wore the blue coat of the Metropolitans, while Alva makes much of his bright blue eyes. Neither knows why he left the police force, or whether he was kicked out. "He wasn't one of the worst," Alva says. "He never cracked heads except when he had to." I rub my bruised elbow and stay quiet.

Alva glances at the wall clock and sighs, then stands to adjust her clothing and hair. The theatres and music-halls will let out soon, spilling men onto the streets, men lusting after the dancers and actresses they cannot touch, and Alva will be waiting for them.

Nettie also stands. She wears a green dress from a time when her hair was fiery red instead of clay-brown. She still enjoys a walk among the night-time crowds and, every now-and-then, a man will recognize her, treat her to a drink for old times' sake.

~

Two days later, well past noontime, Blue John pulls me from the tavern and hands me a stack of papers tied with twine. We walk to Waterloo Bridge station, where clerks and merchants swarm the platform awaiting the late afternoon trains.

"Watch and learn." Blue John cuts the twine and grabs a few sheets. He tips back his derby and shouts "Murder!" before wading into the crowd and thrusting a page into the startled face of a man half his size. "There's a fiend on the prowl, my friend, read all the shocking details the *Times* won't tell, only a ha'penny." I follow, handing papers to Blue John until a train arrives and drains our customers away.

Blue John counts out thirty sheets and holds them up. "Ha'penny each. So how much is this lot worth, then?"

"Fifteen pence," I say. "I know my numbers and I can read, too. Before Mother died I went to the poor school most every day."

The corners of Blue John's mouth twitch. He hands me the sheets. "Don't give 'em the paper until you have their coin."

The station grows crowded and I find my voice. I learn the game of catching men's eyes, finding those eager to buy, sensing which ones will shy away. One man hands over a penny and, seeing the train chuffing at platform's edge, leaves without his change. I give Blue John fifteen pence and keep what's left over. He gives me another thirty sheets. We're out of paper before the six o'clock train arrives.

On the way home Blue John motions for me to walk beside him. "You like it, don't you," he says, "yelling bloody murder, taking their money."

I nod. I like the yelling, and the ha'penny hidden in my pocket. I like being away from the tavern's endless chores and Father's silence. Which part I like best, I'm not sure.

"Show me your hands."

For a heartbeat I think he knows about the coin. I raise my hands, fingers splayed.

"Mr. Knows-his-numbers. Perhaps I'll teach you to set type."

~

I stand at the work desk in Blue John's room, holding the composing stick—a small open-topped metal box—as he reads out words from his journal. I pick type pieces from a desk drawer and arrange them, left-to-right and upside-down, in the stick. The raised letters appear backwards to the eye but will print right on paper. I am still slow at setting the type, though I can now read the topsy-turvy letters as fast as I can read a newspaper sheet.

The story tells of a Temperance Union worker, her throat slashed, her body left on the steps of the police station in Hyde Park. Blue John reads out the next sentence: *Neither her piety nor her high-necked woolen dress protected her from the fiend's attack.*

Blue John checks my completed lines and adds them to a block of type waiting in the galley. Then, impatient to be done, he moves the journal to the desktop and takes over typesetting. He works quickly, despite his broad hands and blunt fingers.

"There was a man," I say, breaking the silence, "a shopkeeper, beaten to death in Alewife Lane this morning. You could do his story tomorrow."

"A shopkeeper? Finch, I'm disappointed," Blue John says. "I thought you knew how this game works. Our readers don't want simple violence. They want sensation—a shiver of fear, a peek into a stranger's dirty secrets. This story," he points to the half-filled galley, "will sell. A well-born victim, a good girl workin' with the downtrodden, her life snuffed out by an unknown killer. Oh yes, I like this story. Fear and titillation and blood. That's what we sell."

"How do you find the stories? Before the newspapers even print them?"

"I was a copper for ten years, weren't I? I still have friends on the force, at the morgue. And friends on the other side as well—pawnbrokers, pickpockets, rag-and-bone men. They know who's doing what in the dark, in the alleyways." He sets the final lines of type into the galley, binds the lines together with a length of cord, and transfers it to an iron-framed chase. "And what I don't know, I can always make up," Blue John adds. "Readers don't want facts, they want a story. The killing is just the first act. Then comes capture and confession, a trial and a hanging. All good grist for our mill."

I think of the Temperance worker, hurrying through the dark. Did she know what was happening? Did she try to scream, through her gaping throat?

"This press was my father's," Blue John continues. He inserts blocks of wood and wedge-shaped quoins into the chase to lock the story in place, then places a board over the top and gently taps the surface with a mallet to level the type. "Da was a jobber-printer, never did anything original in his life. He loved ink and drink, and nothing else. Wanted me to be a printer, but I had other ideas." Blue John puts the mallet down and takes up the ink knife.

By the time I leave for my evening chores the clank and thump of the letterpress fills the cellar. Blue John's leg pumps up and down, the inky rollers stroke across the letters, the platen thrusts against the bed of type. Blue John feeds in blank white paper with his right hand and removes printed stories with his left. The ink will dry by morning.

~

We fall into a routine. Twice a week we work the train stations. Other days Blue John walks the streets, talks to his friends, or visits pubs to listen to gossip and rumors. I start bringing a pail of beer to his room in the evening. Some nights he motions me inside, pulls open the desk drawers and teaches me about the different typefaces, the serifs and grotesques, blackletters and gothics. He speaks lovingly of their beaks and barbs, shoulders and spines, loops, links and tails. Other nights he takes the beer and shuts the door without a word, and I return to my room to peek through the floorboards, to watch him remove the red leather journal from its hiding place atop the wardrobe. He writes, reads, strikes out passages and reconsiders. Some nights he is well-pleased with his scribblings, other nights he seems angry. Some nights he rises, puts on the policeman's coat, and leaves until dawn.

~

The weather turns cold, proper November weather. My numb fingers clutch the handles of a barrow as we deliver to the news agents who now buy our pages and offer them for sale right next to the *Times* and *Telegraph*. Blue John speaks of hiring other boys, of teaching them what we share and sending them out to the train stations under my supervision.

We turn a corner and meet Nettie coming from market, a basket on her arm. "Afternoon," Blue John says, tipping his hat and extending a sheet toward her. "A free copy for you, my dear." His shirt cuffs are grimy and his fingers black with ink. Nettie thrusts the paper into her basket and hurries past.

Blue John snorts. "The good woman is disgusted. Yet she still reads." He grabs my shoulder and pulls me around to face him. "Know this, Finch, I won't stay a penny-pamphleteer for long. Mr. Dickens gets rich spewing out sentimental tripe, stories of orphans and lost fortunes, all nonsense. The people want murder and by God I will give it to them."

~

Blue John writes furiously. I watch, drifting in and out of sleep, until he replaces the journal in its hiding spot and takes down the blue coat. As he leaves I rise and creep into the pantry, where I nick Father's keys, a stub of candle, and a matchbox.

The red leather of the journal is smooth and supple, warm to the touch. Inside are Blue John's notes, drafts of stories, sketches of victims. I start at page one and struggle to read his disorderly handwriting. I fear his return and do not stay long.

~

I cannot keep away from the red leather journal. I live for the nights Blue John puts on the police coat. I stay longer and longer in his room, burning through candles and risking discovery, learning how he puts together his stories.

~

It's early December, and full dark by five o'clock. The tavern's gas lamps are blazing. Nettie and Alva sit at their usual table, heads together, talking over their drinks.

"*You* probably already know," Nettie says to me as I sit down. "Two souls killed Sunday night, a man—"

"An Earl, almost seventy years old," interrupts Alva.

"—and his mistress, a dancer, barely sixteen. They found the bodies together, naked, behind the stage at the Alhambra."

I don't say anything. I've been out with Blue John all afternoon, selling the Earl's story. A good murder. Profitable.

Nettie shakes her head. "Horrible what they say in the papers. No respect for the dead." She stares straight at me.

Blue John approaches across the tavern floor. He wears a gamboge waistcoat and carries a new walking stick, its ivory handle already smudged with ink. "Evening," he says, removing his hat, looking only at Alva.

"Oh, leave us alone," Nettie says.

"Don't tell me what to do, Old whore."

"You think that's an insult?" Nettie's blood is up. "It's truth. Men gave me money to stay with them, and gifts when they tired of me, and I saved it all. What did the police give you? A boot up the arse?"

Blue John's face goes quiet. He nods to Alva before walking away.

"Why'd you rile him?" Alva says. "He isn't a copper anymore, he's a businessman. An author." She stares after him, then sighs and stands.

My stomach clenches, hard, and I grab Alva's hand. "Don't go out tonight," I beg. "It's cold. Why not try working at something different?" I feel flushed and stupid.

Alva pulls her hand free and pats my head. "You're a sweet boy. But I was a seamstress once, and I ain't about to go back to it. Twelve hours work for a single shilling. No, I'll make my living using what God gave me, using it how men want." She pushes past me and heads for the door.

"You're one to talk, Finch," Nettie snaps. "Why do you work with *him*? He's a brute and he's turning you into one, too."

I feel tears rising, of anger and hurt and something I can't name, and I turn on Nettie. "He's just giving men what they want, Nettie. Like you did. Like Alva does."

Nettie slams down her drink and hurries after Alva. I take her glass to the scullery, where Father hides the good whiskey. Up in my storeroom I sip whiskey and watch over Blue John as he writes. When he stands and puts on the policeman's coat I wrap my blanket around my head, to muffle the call of the journal.

I dream of blood and conquest, and wake to the smell of frying liver drifting up from the cellar. Blue John is at work, his mallet tapping on a form filled with type. I go to help, but Blue John is inking the disc by the time I stumble through his doorway. He grins and gives me the meat scraps in his skillet.

"Why so early?" I ask.

"I want the ink dry by noon," he says. "We'll be first on this one—a good bloody murder last night, in Soho Square. No one important, but gruesome. We'll sell at Kings Cross."

Before I can ask about the story I hear Father in the courtyard, calling my name. I leave the cellar and crouch in the stairwell until Father gives up, then I run through the streets to Soho Square. Constables cluster around a pile of green rags heaped on pavement black with blood. Other coppers keep the gawkers away. Next to me two housemaids stand and stare, baskets clutched tight.

"Murder!" I shout. The coppers glare at me and I take off running, pleased with how the maids jumped and gasped.

That afternoon a light snow begins to fall as we work the street in front of Kings Cross. My patter is automatic now—I no longer hear the words I shout. A man wearing a black satin cravat hands over tuppence, his lips wet and eager. I turn away without giving him change. Old fool. I tuck a sheet into my trouser pocket, to read later.

In the evening the tavern is quiet, though snow usually brings in customers eager to warm up, to drink and sing. Alva sits by herself in the corner.

"Where's Nettie?" I ask.

Alva pats the bench. "Slide over close to me, love," she says, and puts her arm around my shoulders. "Nettie's not coming back." She runs her fingers through my hair, but it tugs and pulls, not like when Nettie does it.

"She's not?" A heaviness settles in my chest.

"No, Finch. She's dead. They found her body this morning."

My hand goes to my back pocket. I pull out the sheet but the disobedient letters jump and tremble, and I stumble over the words. When I get to the part about Nettie being carved up, her kidneys and liver gone, I bolt into the courtyard and drop to my knees, retching. Steam rises from my puke and I think of Nettie, of her body growing cold in the dark while Blue John set down her story. *No one important, but gruesome.* He'd made sure of that.

Father, on his way to the privy, sees me kneeling on the bricks. He tells me to get up, that there's work to be done.

~

I'm behind the bar, shucking oysters. Blue John sits with Alva. I watch them as I pry open shells, cut through tough muscle, spill out slick gray meat. Father has told me that Blue John will leave the cellar at month's end, that he's starting a reporter's job at the *Dispatch*. No more inking the press for him, no need to hawk papers at the railway station with a boy by his side.

I force a smile and carry a plate of oysters to Blue John. His new waistcoat is striped ivory-and-crimson and his hands are scrubbed raw, but crescents of ink remain under his fingernails. Alva snuggles close, clutching his arm. Blue John and Alva. I watch them later, through the floorboards.

~

I hate waiting, watching Blue John fondle the supple red leather at night. Five days pass before he takes down the policeman's coat and I am able to visit the journal. I turn to the final pages, where the letters are clear and bright, jostling each other for the chance to be read. They describe the alleyways behind the Haymarket, tell me where Blue John will wait tonight in the dark. I fetch Father's razor and a slender fish knife. They quiver in my hands, like birds eager to fly, not at all like the obedient weight of a composing stick filled with type. When I find Blue John I'll call out his name. '*It's only Finch*,' he'll think, and stop for me. '*No danger. Just a boy.*'

I'll do what needs to be done, then hurry home to my type and press. *Shocking Murder; Police Imposter*! The words are already tumbling into place in my head. I'll write the story, lock the type, tell what I choose to tell. It will be a good murder, and a fine first act.

D.K. Wayrd lives in a kudzu-infested corner of North Carolina with one spouse, various animals, and an alter ego who writes science fiction and fantasy. Wayrd's horror stories have published in *Phobos* and the anthology *Zombified*.

Post-Modern Pea Soup
A Conversation with Paul Tremblay

by Catherine Grant

Paul Tremblay has been writing horror, dark fantasy and science fiction since the early 2000's. He has published three novels with ChiZine, the latest a collaboration with Stephen Graham Jones called *Floating Boy and the Girl Who Couldn't Fly*. He also helps administrate the Shirley Jackson Awards.

I was at Boskone in 2014 when I met Paul. My fiancée, Barry, had met him a few times at other events and there at Boskone he asked how Paul was doing, any news lately? Paul got as giddy as a schoolboy before summer vacation, his smile stretching full across his face. I half expected him to float away as he told us he had "something big," but that he didn't have the go-ahead to tell anyone yet. Barry and I both looked at each other, shrugged, and gave him our congratulations anyway.

When his book deal with William Morrow was announced, I wasn't just excited for Paul, I was excited for the horror genre as a whole. I was excited for myself, for Shock Totem, for every single horror author I know who dreams of scoring a book deal with a major publisher. There is an impression out there, hanging above the genre like a thick, grey cloud, that horror just doesn't sell to big publishers anymore, and here was an author proving that completely wrong.

When I was able to get my hands on a copy of *A Head Full of Ghosts*, I ripped through it at breakneck speed, a reading pace usually reserved for fluff. This book is *not* fluff. It is a fresh, postmodern look at the demonic possession trope that has existed since the succubus of medieval folklore, but really emerged into popular fiction with the book and film *The Exorcist*.

Paul was very generous to give Shock Totem some of his time so that we could discuss his love of horror and the inspiration behind *A Head Full of Ghosts*.

~

CG: So I just wanted to start out by saying that I just finished reading *A Head Full of Ghosts*, and I loved it.

PT: Great! I'm glad you liked it.

CG: You've been getting a lot of good reviews on Goodreads. I don't want to spoil this book for anybody, but I feel like that might be easy, so please stop me from any potential spoilers. I loved how you had, in parallel, the mental illness and the horror elements. Barry and I talked about the book afterwards, because we both read it at the same time, and we had completely

different perspectives on what happened.

PT: Oh, cool!

CG: I feel like readers, depending on her or his beliefs, could see the events unfolding in a different way. Was that your intention?

PT: That's a good question. I definitely wanted to try to write it so there would be the both sides. I really tried to write it so there could be an argument for a secular explanation, or for a supernatural explanation, without being too annoying. I ended the novel saying, "Here, I'll answer some questions," but I knew I was going to sort of leave "the big question" unanswered. I don't think that's really a spoiler; I've told a lot of people that. It's like that through the whole book, you know, is she possessed or is she suffering from a psychotic break or something? I've been very pleased that people, so far, have really responded to that.

I went into writing it thinking I was going to write a "secular exorcism" novel; I really didn't want to write a novel where the church or the priest rolled in and saved the day, you know, like what usually happens in Hollywood movies. There's no real good guys in the book; everybody's making their mistakes.

A friend of mine, Dave Zeltserman, wrote a book called *The Caretaker of Lorne Field*, and I thought he did a great job. It's a short novel, and it's about this guy whose family is supposed to be in charge of taking care of this field and pulling weeds every week, and if they don't pull these weeds, the local legend is that the weeds turn into giant monsters that destroy the world. It's such a fun book. He's a crime writer, and he has a skill set that a lot of horror writers don't have; he has that ability to play with that mystery aspect of that. Is [the main character] really saving the world, or is he really crazy and believes that these plants are going to come alive? He does a great job keeping that going all the way to the end of the book. So, story wise, the two books are definitely not like each other, but that tension of what's real and what's not is definitely inspired by Dave's book.

CG: Do you feel your own beliefs came into play with this, or were you trying to remain impartial, to try to ride that thin line?

PT: There's definitely a bit of my belief system in this book, and especially in how I approached it. When people ask me, I say it's a "post-modern secular exorcism novel." I really wanted to take a very critical view of how organized religion has treated, throughout history, these people that have been afflicted with...or they claim to be possessed. I personally believe that they're mentally ill. I would say I do not, in real life, believe in possession; but it's different than what do I believe *in fiction*.

I can certainly be made to believe that in fiction, so I wanted to approach it from that angle. I tried to be fair and objective; I certainly didn't paint, within the novel, vivid references to her therapist, either. There's no shining white knight or heroes within the novel that save Marjorie; pretty much all of the adults make terrible decisions as their whole family sort of caves to their own personal sort of hell.

CG: I know you had a short story in your collection *In the Mean Time* (2010), called "Growing Things," that has a lot of similarities to this novel.

PT: Yeah, I definitely sort of ended up re-using that story; it became this distinctly thematic thing. When I wrote this novel, I had sort of a three-part structure in mind; I sort of knew where I wanted to go with the ending—not exactly *how* to get there, but I knew I wanted to get to a certain spot. But when I set out to write it, I had no idea I was going to use "Growing Things," but when the sisters started telling stories, it occurred to me that I could use a story I had already written. I've done that a couple of times; there's a story in the same collection called "There's No Light Between Floors," and I ended up sort of cannibalizing that story in my novel *The Little Sleep* (2008). I mean, it's my stuff, I can use it, right?

CG: Absolutely! I think reading "Growing Things" after the novel gave me a different perspective. In the story, especially in the beginning, you know the father is mentally ill, whereas in *A Head Full of Ghosts*, it's kind of a question that lingers in the back of your mind throughout the book.

PT: Yeah, I really wanted to try [that]. I also kind of have lots of, you know, like DVD "Easter Eggs"—I feel like [if] people really get into the book, they'll find the "Growing Things" story. And actually, there's a pretty good chance that my publisher might re-distribute "Growing Things" later this summer, like for a dollar online. So that would be a pretty cool thing for people to find after they read the novel.

Without giving too much away, most of the character's names, especially their last names, are named after different characters in horror films, horror literature. To me, this book is sort of my "big horror novel"—my love-letter to horror. I feel like I put my lifetime of reading and writing horror into that novel. So as I mentioned, various characters' last names are from horror characters. I don't want to give too much away, but Merry, her name, Meredith, is a nod to Shirley Jackson's Meriadoc, from *We Have Always Lived In the Castle*; Marjorie, her name came from Stewart O'Nan's great novel *The Speed Queen*—and actually, I included Stewart and Shirley in my dedication to the book, so…that's sort of what I did, I wanted to take my sort of "path" in horror and use it all, if I could.

CG: When I was reading *A Head Full of Ghosts*, **I was reminded of a quote from Stephen King, where he talks about why he likes writing children characters in his books, and how the most terrifying people in their lives are, most of the time, the adults around them. How do you feel about writing children characters in those kinds of situations?**

PT: I'm totally fascinated with and by children characters. My writing took a turn in that direction after the birth of my first child, and definitely after my second child. So many of my short stories, especially in *In the Mean Time*, either involve children from their point of view, or there's certain children in the family; there's certainly stories about the anxieties of being a new parent not knowing what to do. It's such a big part of my life, especially since I didn't start messing around with writing until my mid-twenties, right around the same time I was just getting married... So it's almost been like that part of my life has just coincided almost exactly with becoming a writer, so it's been a theme [and] concern throughout all of my writing.

I feel like, for me, I still remember childhood and how I thought as a child. In a lot of ways, I still don't feel like an adult, actually. I think a lot of adults come to that realization at some point in their lives, which is really hard for [them], because it's like, "There's no adults, there's just us." To me, that's a weird thing. You think you know all the answers, and you take a certain measure of comfort in that, even though there is plenty of evidence to the contrary that the adults do not have all the answers.

I think that King quote is great. To me, my favorite part of horror literature is the answer to the question: if this happens to you, whatever this happens to be, what are you going to do? What decisions are you going to make? How are you, how is anybody, going to live through this? I think when horror is done correctly, horror is really equipped to address those questions in very interesting ways.

CG: In the context of writing horror, how do you feel writing an adult book like *A Head Full of Ghosts* **is different than writing a young adult book, such as** *Floating Boy*?

PT: You know, to be honest, we were sort of writing on the fly, at least I was, in terms of writing YA. I kept trying to go by a specific guideline of "I'm not going to swear." You know, trying to keep everything through the point of view of teens and their world, and not try to go with the parents too often. So I was concerned about the voice and just tried to be realistic to the teenage experience, I guess. I've been around teens every day for my day job, so I kind of feel like, at least with the teens of New England, I've had experience with how they are, how they act, and sort of what they think. I guess I feel more comfortable writing adult-style fiction, but it's not really a conscious thing.

For *A Head Full of Ghosts*, there are young protagonists, I didn't censor or shy away from any kind of uncomfortable question that would come up. There's a lot of stuff in *A Head Full of Ghosts* that I wouldn't put into the *Floating Boy* novel.

CG: I had a question about Karen Brisette, a real-life blogger and reviewer. I thought it was interesting that you used a real-life person in the book. Why did you decide to do that?

PT: Yeah, I've been a fan of her reviews on Goodreads, and we've interacted a bit. She really liked my collection *In the Mean Time*, and was a big champion for it, so I was very grateful. I really liked the style of her reviews, and there are very few times that I like nonfiction. I kind of feel like hers and my styles are pretty similar; not the same, but a little bit similar, in terms of the enthusiasm; she's just funny and clever. So I was looking for a name, and I think up people's names all the time. I'm sure you noticed Barry Lee Dejasu's first name in there…

CG: Yeah!

PT: I almost used Barry's whole name! I actually named other characters after people; I ended up changing a bunch of them at different points, but Barry's stayed, and Karen Brisette's stayed. I thought it would be cool if someone were to, again, look back on the book and go, "Hey, who's this character?" Keep messing with people after the book is over, you know?

CG: I remember you telling me at last year's Boskone that you had "this cool news, but I can't tell anybody right now."

PT: Yeah, I'd just found out the week before.

CG: Well, when you announced the book deal with William Morrow for *Head Full of Ghosts*, I thought to myself, "Well, no *wonder* he was so excited!"

For so long, we horror writers had our own little niche, and I feel like it's been such a long time since we've had a book like that in the mainstream. Do you feel like that's changing, like the horror market might expand, and horror books might break out in the next few years?

PT: "Break out" is such a loaded term, but I do think that speculative fiction in general is a little more represented in the mainstream nowadays, with the success of Jeff VanderMeer last year, his collection got a huge response from the mainstream. There's tons of well-known authors who are considered literary, [but who write] genre work.

I was working on another novel, I was a hundred pages into it, when I had the idea for *A Head Full of Ghosts*. This was in February 2013; at the time, we had a couple of fairly big mainstream literary takes on zombies; Colson Whitehead's *Zone One*, for instance, which is an excellent novel. Glen Duncan, another "literary" author, had his werewolf trilogy, and Benjamin Pierce also had a werewolf novel (*Red Moon*), so we had sort of a literary update on werewolves, and vampires are always there, so I thought, no one has written a literary update on *The Exorcist*.

So I had that idea, and the two sisters sort of occurred to me, and one of my favorite bands, Bad Religion, had just come out with a song called "My Head Is Full of Ghosts." So I started thinking on that and put the other book away, which at the time I thought was a really hard decision; I was a hundred pages into it, and it was kind of intimidating to start from scratch again, but once I got going into [*A Head Full of Ghosts*], it was fun. It was as fun as writing can be; it's always more fun in retrospect, because when you're in the middle of it, it's not as fun.

There were definitely parts of the book I really enjoyed writing. I had a lot of fun with the blog posts; they weren't like the greatest thing ever, but I think that people can tell my enthusiasm for horror in general was in there.

CG: So is the book you got a hundred pages into going to be the next thing you'll work on? Because *A Head Full of Ghosts* is obviously a stand-alone book; it's not going to be a series.

PT: No, I'm actually doing something different. I'm working on a novel [*Disappearance at Devil's Rock*] that revolves around a thirteen-year-old boy who goes missing from a state park in Massachusetts, and it sort of goes from there. So I'm in the middle of that; that's due in July.

CG: You had a collaboration as well, with Stephen Graham Jones, *Floating Boy and the Girl Who Couldn't Fly*.

PT: Yeah, that came out last November in the U.S.

CG: Are you going to do any other collaboration with other authors?

PT: I don't know; nothing's planned, but I've done collaboration on two short stories, and the novel with Stephen Graham Jones. All the collaborations are sort of spur-of-the-moment, spontaneous, kind of, "Hey, why don't we try this?" So while I have no definite plans to do so, I'm certainly not planning to *not* do it.

Especially writing with Stephen was a lot of fun. He's so talented, and it was really easy; our styles are kind of, if not similar, then compatible to sort of mash together and not be too unreadable. He was just so fun to work with. He writes so fast, so that was the only hard part. I'd be working so hard and slaving over it, and sending him a chapter every couple of weeks, and he'd have his part like a day later.

CG: Do you have any plans to edit any more anthologies, like *Phantom* and *Creatures*?

PT: I have no real plans for it. I'm surprised at how much time those took up. It was a lot of fun, especially to work with John Langan and Sean Wallace; I just find that to work in a team to pick stories is a lot more work than people imagine. I enjoyed it, but I'm very much all hands on deck for this next novel for William Morrow.

CG: Do you think the character Mark Genovich (of *The Little Sleep* and *No Sleep 'Till Wonderland*) will ever return?

PT: I'd say it's unlikely. The only thing that could bring him back, potentially I suppose—pie in the sky stuff again—but if Hollywood comes calling and wants to pick it up as a television series, which my agent has been pitching for a while; or if the publisher comes back and said they'd like to see another one, then maybe; but otherwise, I have no plans to do so. The publisher at the time, Henry Holt, wasn't interested in a third one, and neither was I, at that point in time. I totally envisioned *The Little Sleep* as a one-book thing, and even when I turned the book in to my agent, I told him, "Look, I understand the publisher is looking for series, especially for genre works, but this is the only book that I'm writing." I told him that, and he said, "Yeah-yeah-yeah." So we got the book deal; there are much bigger problems in life than having to write a second book featuring the same character, so I'm glad I wrote *No Sleep 'Till Wonderland*. I think it's a really good book. They'd have to come to me and say, "We *have* to have this third book, we will make you do it!"

CG: Is there any genre or topic that you would want to take on in one of your future novels or short stories?

PT: Nothing comes to mind. I tend to... I don't know if it's the math part of my brain, but I tend not to be swimming with tons of different ideas, but I know some of my friends have this list of ideas that they can pull from or go to and sort of plan out what they're going to write for the next five years, but I just don't operate that way. I can't even really work on two things at once. Even when I'm writing novels, it's really difficult for me to go away to a short story; I basically shut down the novel and write the short story; you know, don't pick up the novel again until after I'm done with the short story. So I feel like when I get an idea and I feel like it's worth exploring with my writing, I just kind of obsess about it, focus totally in on it, really to the point that I shut out everything else. I wouldn't necessarily advocate for that as a way to go, but this is kind of how I work; even if I wanted to change it, I would have a hard time changing it. I wouldn't mind writing a really cool giant monster sort of book.

CG: And you're still working as a teacher, correct?

PT: Yup; still a full-time teacher. I teach math and I coach a couple of sports at school. That's part of the deal for the faculty; we have to coach a couple of sports. But the school is pretty supportive of my writing, so hopefully that keeps going.

CG: Do you see yourself ever stopping your day job, so to speak? I think everybody dreams of that, you know, quitting their day job and writing full-time; do you think you'd ever want to do that?

PT: Pie in the sky, definitely. I can't imagine the pressure of "I have to write this novel, so I feed my family." I'm extremely impressed by talented folks like Christopher Golden, and writers in general who write for a living. I just imagine it must be really difficult to produce not just because you *want* to produce, but because you *have* to produce. So, maybe someday, but I'm trying to do one book at a time at this point. I definitely feel that pressure, because [with] *A Head Full of Ghosts*, I made the best book that I could.

I'd be lying if I said that in my low time, I wasn't like, "Oh, this isn't as good as *A Head Full of Ghosts*; what's gonna happen?" The book I'm writing right now is completely different from this one, so it's hard to compare the two. They're both horror novels, but different kinds of horror novels. I think it's what really every writer struggles with, the comparisons to earlier work, but not that I can't get better.

CG: I was thinking about *Swallowing a Donkey's Eye* and how completely different it is from *A Head Full of Ghosts*. Do you feel less or more freedom being with a different kind of publisher, writing such a completely different book than what you've written previously?

PT: Well, not really. That novel, *Swallowing a Donkey's Eye*, I sort of had in draft form kicking around for quite a little bit. Some of that book is some of the first stuff I'd written. It was really like seven years from when I started it to re-writing it for the final time and sending it to ChiZine. So that book was totally a labor of love; I was under no delusion that that would sell huge, because it's such a wacky book. Sort of my ode to Kurt Vonnegut and his wonderful wackiness.

With William Morrow, I mean, there's freedom to a certain point, I guess; they want literary horror novels from me, so I'm happy to write in that for now. So I wouldn't be able to turn in stuff like *Swallowing a Donkey's Eye*; they do have horror expectations for the next book.

CG: Of course, if you *did* have something else like *Swallowing a Donkey's Eye*, you have still have a relationship with ChiZine that you could take it to.

Yeah, I mean; as far as that stuff, one of the usual signs of working with ChiZine is you have total freedom of creativity. Certainly, they'll edit the books and [we go] back and forth like that, but in terms of storyline or how strange it gets or has gotten, they go with it, so that's one of the wonderful things working with ChiZine.

So actually, that book that I put away, the hundred pages, it's not quite like *Swallowing a Donkey's Eye*, but there's certainly an irreverence to it. It's probably a little bit less mainstream, which is part of the reason why I put it away and haven't gotten back to it yet. But I think I will go back to it at some point.

CG: In *A Head Full of Ghosts*, there were mentions of H.P. Lovecraft, and I was curious as to whether he was an influence of yours?

PT: It's funny, I'm much more influenced by friends and colleagues who were very much influenced by Lovecraft, like Laird Barron and John Langan. There are so many contemporary authors who have been influenced by Lovecraft, or if not Lovecraft per se, then by the idea of cosmic horror.

Anyway, going into *A Head Full of Ghosts,* like we talked about how I wanted to have a question, "Is there a supernatural explanation, or is it just secular?" So even when it came to the supernatural explanation, I didn't necessarily want to have a rote demon kind of thing; so I threw in some references to Lovecraft to maybe hint [that Marjorie] maybe is possessed by something older than time itself, older than what Christian mythology has to offer.

CG: Have you read anything lately that you really enjoyed, or want to talk about?

PT: I'm reading *Hausfrau* right now, by Jill Alexander Nussbaum, which is like an update of [Tolstoy's] *Anna Karenina*. This is her first novel, but she is a very accomplished poet, so the prose is just gorgeous. Basically, the story is about a dissatisfied wife living in Switzerland, having affairs with different men; so it's not like a thriller with a high-pitched plotline, it's a character study with very good writing, and it's pretty dark, too.

In the past month, I also read Daphne du Maurier's *Don't Look Now*; I've never actually read any Daphne du Maurier, which was something that I had to rectify. The short story, "The Birds," was just...I mean, perfect; I had no idea. I'd seen the Hitchcock film version of it, which is actually nowhere near as good as the short story. Her collection is very mixed, which is awesome.

CG: I do have to ask you, Paul...there is a rumor that you hate pickles. Why?

PT: I don't know...I just really hate them. There's sort of an odd story where... I hated pickles before this, though, but I'm not making this up. This actually happened.

One of my childhood friends had a sister in elementary school, grade school; she babysat me and my brother and sister a couple of times. There was one night, she was babysitting, and her friend was also over, and they must've been high or something, but I woke up and they were giggling, and something wet by my ear, and it was a pickle in my ear. While I was sleeping.

CG: Congratulations, you've managed to put tension in a story about pickles.

PT: Great...

CG: Is there anything you'd like to add?

PT: I feel so protective of some of the twists of different things that happened in [*A Head Full of Ghosts*]; I don't want to give too much away.

I guess I actually encourage people who read horror would get a lot out of this book, especially with the relationship between Merry and Marjorie; most of the early readers have really connected with how those sisters interact in their relationship. I hope most people who really aren't horror readers will read the book, too.

CG: Thank you so much for doing this interview!

PT: Sure, thanks! I appreciate it.

Three Years Ago This May

by Trace Conger

Henry wants to die today. He doesn't think I know what's going on in that head of his, but I do. Forty-three years of marriage and raising three children together will do that to you. I've been able to read his mind for as long as I can remember. Can finish his sentences most of the time, too.

Every morning at our summer cabin had been the same since we retired and bought the place eight years ago. Henry gets up at the crack of dawn, downs a cup of the blackest coffee he can brew, kisses me good morning, and then sets out on his canoe trip across the lake and back. It takes him about an hour. If he stops on the lake to feed the ducks, it's an hour and fifteen.

We've got two canoes tied to the dock. The scratched-to-Hades aluminum one came with the place. One of the seats is broken and it's prone to tip with the slightest shift in weight. The other, a green fiberglass canoe, came courtesy of the Adirondack Conservation Society raffle two years ago. It's got padded seats and doesn't bounce as much on the water.

I used to have my own morning ritual. After watering down his brew, I'd sit on the back porch in my thatched rocking chair and flip through the stack of *Adirondack Life* magazines we'd collected over the years. I'd look up every few minutes to see how much progress Henry had made on the lake. After two cups of coffee, I'd head for the kitchen, fire up the stove, and watch him from the kitchen window. When Henry returned, we'd enjoy breakfast and then talk about what we were going to do for the rest of the day. Maybe head into town, visit with friends, read in front of the fire, or just sit around and do nothing. Same routine. Every morning. Every summer.

Sometimes Henry sits on the back porch and knocks squirrels out of the pine trees with his .22. He keeps the handgun in a black and yellow plastic toolbox next to the back door. I don't like the killing, but squirrels can make a mess of the place in the offseason. They get inside the cabin and settle into the mattresses. They rip up the furniture and scratch the walls. One year, they even chewed through an electrical cord. We arrived that June to find two fried squirrels on the kitchen floor.

I stay inside when Henry shoots. Sometimes I instinctively cover my ears when I hear the pop. The .22 doesn't make a loud bang. It sounds more like a small firecracker than a gunshot, but it's unnerving nonetheless. It doesn't have a lot of stopping power, but it gets the job done.

Our morning routine changed after Henry's accident. It was three years ago this May. Some college kid fell asleep at the wheel and collided with Henry's Chevy pickup truck on I-70. The kid lost a few teeth and his football scholarship. Henry lost both his legs. Severed just above the knees.

Ever since the accident Henry has been different. He's the funniest man I know, but I can't remember the last time I saw him laugh. It doesn't help that our children are grown and scattered across the country. Chris in Chicago, Adam in Los Angeles, and Jessica in Minneapolis. They're on their own now and don't have as much time to visit. They don't need us like they used to when they were younger. Sometimes it feels like we're floating out here on our own.

Henry is always eager to get to the cabin come June. He loves the water, but I think it's the absence of other people that really calls him here. There's no one else around to ask if he needs help or if there is anything they can do for him. In the privacy of our cabin, he still has his legs.

The main parts of our morning routine are still there, and the differences are subtle. He doesn't think I notice them, but I do. He still brews his coffee as black as the lake bottom and I still water it down. He still kisses me good morning, but he kisses me longer than he used to. And he's never the first to let go.

Now, he rolls down the worn dirt path being careful not to catch his wheelchair on the exposed tree roots, overgrown ferns, or wild huckleberries. I suggested installing a ramp down to the dock. Insurance would cover it, but Henry said it was out of the question. He said he didn't want to muck up the natural surroundings with a corrugated metal monstrosity. I told him we could get one made out of pine to match the back porch, but the wave of his hand told me I shouldn't bring it up again.

Once he makes it to the dock he maneuvers his wheelchair around the grooves in the planks. He locks the brakes, lowers himself down onto the dock from the wheelchair, and then crawls into the aluminum canoe bobbing in the gentle morning ripples. His red-and-green-checkered flannel blanket is tied tight around his waist. He says he wears it to keep warm, but I know he's really trying to protect me from seeing something he doesn't think I want to see. It never bothered me though.

He tosses the faded orange lifejacket out of the canoe and onto the dock, unties the line, and paddles out. He no longer goes all the way to the other side of the lake. Instead, he paddles a few hundred yards out to the deepest part and sits there. Every morning he seems to stay out a little longer. Thinking.

Henry doesn't know it, but I watch his ritual through the binoculars from the porch. He sets the oar inside the canoe, grips the sides with his hands, leans forward, and waits. Convincing himself of something. That's the moment he makes his decision. Whether to overturn the canoe or not. I think that's why he takes the aluminum canoe. Like I said, it's prone to tip, and maybe one morning the lake will make his decision for him.

Sometimes he turns and stares toward the back porch, sometimes not. But so far, every morning, he's lowered himself back onto the cracked seat, slipped the oar back into the water, turned the canoe around, and paddled back to the dock. Then we make breakfast together.

Of course, my morning routine has changed too. I still water down his brew and I still sit in my thatched rocking chair on the back porch. I no longer thumb through my magazines and I don't start on breakfast while he's on the lake. Instead I watch him through the binoculars. I watch him paddle back to the dock. Once he arrives safe and sound I take the .22 out of my mouth and place it back inside the plastic toolbox.

And sometimes, I even have a third cup of coffee.

Trace Conger is an author in the crime, thriller, and suspense genres. His debut novel, *The Shadow Broker*, follows Mr. Finn, a disgraced PI, as he straddles the fine line between investigator and criminal. Conger lives in Cincinnati. Find him online at www.traceconger.com.

MALEDICTION

by Margaret Killjoy

A night like any night, my bare mattress on the floor, old window glass between me and the street outside. A few bottles on the floor, one filled with piss in the corner—the toilet was three stories down and if there'd ever been a railing there certainly wasn't one now and I'd rather piss into a bottle than break my neck drunk in the dark.

Eduard had come and gone and he'd taken the best of me with him in his mouth and I was spent. I might have even been happy. I'd asked him to stay of course. I always asked him to stay.

"These houses freak me out," he'd said, pulling on his pants both legs at a time with his fat beautiful ass on the edge of my bed.

"Door like mine, cops can't get in," I'd told him. "Not without us hearing."

There was a back way out, too. A window, out onto the neighbor's roof. You could get across a whole city block on rooftops in the right parts of Baltimore.

"Angels can get into this shit," Eduard had told me, and then he'd left. The bar had fallen back down across the door and woken the mice in the walls and cupboards. Eduard spoke street American with a middling-thick German accent and his words had a way of staying in the room after he was gone.

He liked everything about me that I didn't like about myself. He thinks I'm all hardened and shit.

I don't see myself as a graverobber. It's not like that.

She'd died in spring like everyone else. Everyone does it in the springtime. Blood makes the flowers bloom and it melts the snow and it wakes the world from winter. She'd hanged herself, which is kind of classy, isn't it, and there used to be like 600,000 people in this city and now there's less than half of that but the flowers know how to bloom.

Death is really simple for the dead but it's really complicated for everyone else. Ten years now of suicide spring and I'll tell you one thing, the unemployment rate's gone down. Plenty of work for anyone who wants it—it's just that I don't want it.

So I cut her down, that's kind of like work I guess, and I buried her in Druid Hill with the rest of everyone else, and that was definitely work because if you want a free house you'd better at least put in the work to bury its tenants. And I had to put in that door to keep out criminals and cops, but I got friends who helped with that because maybe we're a morbid bunch but at least we help one another out.

It's not graverobbing though. I didn't sell much of her stuff. Nothing that looked personal. I left that stuff in case family ever comes, which it never will.

That old lady's gold jewelry haunts me, though, since there's a *compro oro* place just down the street next to the beer and wine store—I think one guy owns both places, it's hard to tell—and I have to see that gold any time I go into her bedroom, which is basically never. That jewelry haunts me almost as much as she does.

No one knows what it is, but all of a sudden, ten years back, about one in seven of us is going to cut themselves or eat glass or jump off of something they shouldn't. Well, some people say they know what it is. Eduard says he knows what it is. Says his mother told him. She knows it from the old country. I think maybe the old country is Brazil, but maybe it's Germany. Eduard does a lot of things really well but talking about himself isn't one of those things.

There are seven angels returned to the world in anger and vengeance, and they fall prey on everyone in the night and they breathe their curses into our lungs. They fight over every soul. They fight over which of us gets what curse.

But I don't have a soul and neither does anyone I've ever met because the world is full of horror but it's not angelic horror, it's just regular horror, the kind you don't need gods or souls or angels to drum up. Like the look on that woman's face when I cut her down. That's the horror in this world, something that was in her eyes and in her mind that's gone now because she's gone, gone to rot, gone to dust and shadows.

A night like any night, my solar LED lamp spitting out its cum-colored glow on the water-damaged fake wood floor. Some books I'd never read were sitting in a milk crate and the two or three books I read again and again were stacked up near my couch-cushion pillow.

If I got drunk enough, I wouldn't dream about her.

I wouldn't see that face swinging back and forth with the wind of a summer storm coming in through her open window. I wouldn't hear those voices, the conspiratorial whispers, quiet like whispers and mice. I wouldn't hear the rustle of bird wings and or catch the glint of feathers and flesh just past as far as I could see in the dark.

I reached for a bottle. It was empty.

I reached for another. It was empty.

I could stay up till dawn, I decided. But I was at the wrong stage of drunk for that to be true.

You're not supposed to sell beer after midnight in Maryland, but the liquor control board has been hit just as hard by this whole "everyone's dead so no one's working" bit as everywhere else and I was pretty sure the white guy who owned the *compro oro* was going to sell to me or at least the guys he exploited who would be working at that hour might.

I scrambled for my phone and checked my balance. My bank account was as empty as the bottles around me.

I'm not a graverobber but I didn't want to see that lady while I was sleeping so I got up and crept down to the second floor, one hand on the wall because I'm not one-in-seven and I didn't have the slightest desire to teeter off the side of those stairs and land on the floor thirty feet down.

The door to her bedroom was ajar because it was always ajar. If I left it closed the mice would scratch their claws into the wood and by consequence into my eardrums and I didn't like that, so better to just grant them free passage. Most of them live in her bedroom. I think they go out to hunt. I don't want to know what they hunt, but I honestly think its cats. Which is almost too fucked up to think about, a swarm of those little mice getting some stray cornered in the alley, driving it back, one brave mouse leading the charge and ending up dead but its comrades marching on, pouring over the concrete to sink their teeth into mangy flesh. Brave little shits, those mice.

I had my LED lantern in hand. You can't hold it in front of you like a flashlight, you have to hold it back behind your field of vision like a torch. The mice scattered before I could see them as more than just a writing mat on the floor, and I found her dresser. I just took a pair of earrings. That's all, just a pair of earrings. She didn't need them, she was dead. I needed them, because I didn't want to see her while I was sleeping.

I locked up behind me, three keys for three locks and then hit the app on my phone that dropped the bar inside. You can't be too careful—gotta mix hi-tech and low-tech if you want to stay safe. The only light on the street was the blue glow of the cop camera. "We're still here," it's like it was saying. "Everyone you care about is dead and this city is a shell but don't worry, the police are still here. We might help you and we might kill you and you'll never know which it is. But we're here and we can see you."

Some nights I'd talk back to the thing, answer its wordless taunts with wild strings of obscenities. No one can string together obscenities like a street punk faggot, you've got to understand. To half the world, I was an obscenity myself.

But no invectives came to me so I just flashed the cops my cock and kept walking. The *compro oro* was closed and the beer and wine was closed. I was going to keep going, but the thing about flashing a snitch-ass blue light lamppost is that it snitched on me and the cops were coming and I ran the whole way home and got that big beautiful door slammed shut before the cops decided it wasn't even worth leaving their cruiser.

I climbed the stairs by the light of my phone. Even put the earrings back.

Eduard says there are seven angels and they've each got a curse. They can look like anything they want, which usually means they look like anything *we* want, he says. You grow up in America, you're probably going to see them as angels with wings and all that shit. It's what most of us want, I guess. It's like, the American Dream of cursed seraphim.

Eduard said his moms got kissed by the Angel of Longing and she's never been the same and never will be, that for the rest of her life she's going to be missing her sister. But of course she's going to be missing her sister. Her sister is dead now six years, cut up by thugs in the countryside. That wasn't a curse; that was just the shit luck of life.

His grandpa got kissed by the Angel of Sorrow, he says, and the old man spends half his day weeping. There's an Angel of Passion who lets your heart consume itself in the fire of feeling until you've got nothing left and there's an Angel of Harm who obviously got to the lady I buried in the park. There's four others besides, but I'd stopped listening because you can only hear so much of that shit before it starts to get at you.

A night like any night and I lay awake growing more sober by the minute. "Go to sleep," I kept saying, but that's kind of a fuck off bad way to make yourself fall asleep, so it didn't work. I watched headlights drive their way across my wall in big waves of light that crashed into the corners and disappeared faster than they'd come on. There was a lot of traffic at night and sometimes I wondered who was driving and where were they going so late and maybe I wondered what angel had gotten to them or was going to.

Was there an angel of car accidents? It seemed like a lot of people went down in car accidents. But maybe that had always been the case.

There must have been an angel of "you basically won't ever manage to fall asleep after you sober up" because that one had kissed me a long time ago. But there were only seven. Eduard was certain. And if there were only seven angels, their curses were probably a bit less specific or at least a bit more dramatic. I mean, I cut that lady down. She'd hanged herself by the neck and her hands had just been in the pockets of her dress like there was nothing the matter in the world. Like she was out for a Sunday stroll, just walking on air.

Me, if I was hanging from an exposed ceiling beam I'd be clutching and ripping at the rope until my hands were a mess of blood. Maybe that's just me though.

That's how I fell asleep, too, thinking about that lady. Fucking sobriety.

She didn't come into my dreams. Oh, how I wish it'd been her who'd come into my dreams.

He looked something like Eduard. Husky, hairy. He was a bear of an angel. No wings. I guess I believe in sexy men more than I believe in some heavenly host.

I heard him come in and I knew he was there. By the door. Just standing there at my door, watching me. I couldn't see him, not at first. Then a car started past, then it stopped on my street, and in the headlights through my window I could see his thick black beard and the sunken pits that served as his eyes. He was nude, his flaccid cock uncut. He took a step toward me, watching me.

He craned his head to the side like a dog might. He was curious.

Then he smiled, and my body locked up under the power of his gaze.

He walked toward me, his head still cocked. Three purposeful strides and he loomed into the whole of my field of vision. I heard a car door somewhere. The light stayed on my angel.

"Which one are you?" I asked. I couldn't look away, and he straddled my chest. His head shot to attention and I could just barely see his white-blue eyes deep and buried in the darkness cast by his brow.

"No matter where you go," he said, in my voice, "they or someone else will be after you." He leaned down and kissed me, full on the mouth, his tongue caressing my teeth, blood running down from his gums, into my throat.

Then he was gone and I was awake and a police battering ram hit the door. My wondrous door.

I'd bitten deep into my lip and I sat up and wiped blood from my maw. I stared dumbfounded at where he'd been, all the while the battering ram beat out a failed rhythm like some shitty drummer.

I spent a couple breaths pretending like I didn't believe what he'd told me. I mean, it was a dream. I'd been asleep. Real things don't happen when you're asleep, except like pissing your bed or something. But by the time I heard them crash through the door and into the front hall, I knew he'd been telling the truth. They were going to come for me, always.

I scrambled around my room to pack my shit, because I was going to escape, because the only thing worse than running is getting caught. Toothbrush, phone, pants, a book I'd like to say I've read. That's all you need in this world.

I kept a length of rebar by the door to my room. Not in case cops come in. As much as you might want to, you can't hit cops in the face with rebar. I kept it just for, you know, people. In case people came in. I kind of lost some time standing around with that rebar in my hand, trying to figure out if I should take it.

I heard them on the steps. I threw my backpack on and looked in the corner of my room, saw those pee bottles. They were capped. I hoped one of those cops was going to drink my piss. I hoped one of them was going to be like "Fuck, he got away, let's search his shit."

Then his buddy would say "Well he's got a couple 40s of Steel—you want one?" and they would toast and drink that shit. And they'd probably spit it out, right, but what if they didn't?

You've gotta hold onto hope that good things are going to happen in this world.

Instead of finding me gone, though, they found me still there, daydreaming about them drinking my piss. One cop came in, she had a fucking S.W.A.T. shield, and then her buddy came in looking like he owned the place. None of us owned the place.

Then the Angel of Persecution came in behind them, just as naked as he'd been in my dream, and he pointed at me, and he said in my own fucking voice, "There he is."

And that's just not fair, if you ask me, because I was awake.

So I grabbed that rebar and I smashed in that angel's face—or tried to. I got his mouth even bloodier than he'd gotten mine, and I looked again and it wasn't my angel, it was just a uniformed cop. I didn't suppose I'd be able to explain that I hadn't meant to break part of his face with a length of steel rod. I ran.

"Get him!" he yelled, in his own voice, which wasn't anything like my voice. I've got a nice voice. To be fair, he might have had a nice voice before I'd staved in his teeth.

I got a Taser barb in my back for my troubles but only one of them so it didn't complete the circuit and I just kept running and it ripped out of me, I think, and then I was out the window, on the neighbor's roof. I turned around just in time to see a gloved hand on the sill. I brought my bare foot down on it, but that didn't do any good, so I slammed the window shut. That did some good.

People say you can run to fend off panic but it turns out that's not true when you're running across rooftops with three cops behind you firing their handguns—thank fucking God they were mediocre shots or I'd be dead. When I hit the end of the block I failed at some parkour shit I'd seen on YouTube and it's a good thing no one's picked up the trash in a year because otherwise I'd also be dead. Instead, I broke some ribs and the garbage bags broke my fall.

The cops fired a few rounds into the sea of rats and rot around me before they gave up and fucked off. A clean getaway. Nothing to worry about.

Except fingerprints and DNA and that fucking monographed pillow that Eduard had made me back when we were first courting and did nice shit like that for each other. The cops were going to know who I was. That was something to worry about, something I was never going to stop worrying about. Cops are like elephants—they never forget a grudge. Or maybe that's crows.

Cops are worse than crows because they're everywhere, even still.

People say you can run to fend off panic but it's not true when you never stop running.

I see that face everywhere. I've seen him driving a commercial van, and he turned to look at me and waved. He rang me up at the deli once. He's in the background of my selfies, indistinct and leering. He's at shows and bars and he's out of the corner of my eye and sometimes he just straight up attacks me in alleys or shows up with cops and tries to bust me, and he laughs my laugh when I run in fear. It's been two years and I'll never be the same again and I'll never trust anyone because anyone might be him.

I hear him every time I speak. It's no longer him who talks in my voice, it's me who talks in his.

I wish I had guts like that old lady did, but I don't, because here I am on the end of my proverbial rope and I'm scrabbling and ripping at it and my hands are bloody and raw and I'm still breathing.

I'm still breathing, but I'm not sure why.

Margaret Killjoy is an author and editor who travels with no fixed home. Margaret's most recent book is *A Country of Ghosts*, a utopian novel published by **Combustion Books** in 2014.

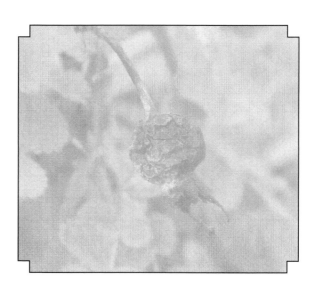

Sweet William

by Mary Pletsch

I sit in Bill's rocking chair and pull back a lace curtain from our living room window. We just bought the curtains last year, but already they're yellowing under the harsh light of the sun glaring through our new windows. I look out into our back yard, studying the trees and wondering why Bill and I didn't have suspicions right away.

The trees on our lot are nothing like the neighbours'. Even the birch across the street, the one that had its top cut off to avoid the power lines, just shot out an arm and continued stretching for the sun like a proper tree should do. Like ours do not.

Our trees stoop almost as soon as they emerge from the ground, angling out and away from our walls as though fleeing contact with the old stone house as soon and as best as they are able. Our pine grows perpendicular to the ground, a bristling barricade between us and the house next door. Bill and I had hoped to save up money and replace the trees eventually, but the young maple that we bought is already mimicking its elders.

Through the floor-to-ceiling windows that flank our front door, I can see that the cedar hedges have spilled over the walk again, growing in gnarled puddles. It's springtime, and the funny dandelions are back. My garden is overgrown with them, not that I got much from it anyway. I am a failure as a nurturer; a failure as a wife.

I wipe at my eyes while I stare at the barren furrows of grey earth, mounded up like graves where I'd planted my garden last spring. At the far end lies a blackened pile of vegetable matter, the decaying fruits of our reaping. At the near end, a few blades of grass wave bravely from the bare earth like intrepid explorers, but mostly the furrows are dotted with the fat columns of what pass for dandelions here.

Each dandelion in our yard is really multiple regular dandelions all squashed together. On close examination, you can see the shapes of where the individual stems should have been before they melted into one. Their stems are thick and gnarled, and they bloom into disgusting mutated heads, with four or more flowers all conjoined. Half of the time they topple under their own weight. Otherwise they sit, bloated and loathsome, atop the lawn they've conquered.

I remember last spring, when we had just moved in to our brand new home—new to us, though the building was old and in need of repairs. We were so eager to grow our own food, so eager to start again. Drunk on optimism, we overlooked the strawberries that grew as blackened, shriveled knots on the vine, and the spinach that shot out thousands of narrow leaves until we wondered whether it was spinach at all or whether we'd planted something else by accident. We were new at this gardening business, and it was inevitable we'd make some mistakes.

Bill and I told ourselves that we'd been overly ambitious when we thought things would look like the pictures in my gardening book. Leaves more green than yellow, and stems growing in spirals against the ground, and roots that burst from the earth and draped themselves over leaves—perhaps these things were, if not *normal*, at least within the realm of expectation. Strange things surely happened from time to time. Editors would remove the ugly accidents from their books; photographers would choose their most appealing pictures. We'd been fed false expectations on glossy pages. Reality was bound to have a few warts.

Still, as the summer wore on, we looked at the soft green sacs we'd believed would ripen into tomatoes, watched as the flies lit on their wrinkled skin and the liquid within quivered, and decided perhaps we ought not eat those. We pulled raspberries off vines, risking thorns, and discovered furry clots of mold within. Maybe we'd used too much weed killer, or not enough fertilizer. Maybe the garden needed better drainage. Maybe we should just try again next year.

Everything soured last year, rotting on the vine. Bill got a summer cold, hacking and spitting as he leaned low over our riding lawnmower and tried to cut the grass, wheezing and gasping when he took the blades off the mower to sharpen them yet again. I couldn't keep up with the repairs and the housework and the garden and my job besides, so we let the lawn grow wild.

By fall, though, there was no contesting our harvest. The fat promise of corn ears, shucked, revealing doubled cobs covered all over with blue blight. Zucchini, cut, spilled forth pale yellow slime like perverse cordon bleu. Potatoes, dug, pulled from their burial mounds beneath withered, stinking stalks. We exhumed not five or six hand-size tubers, but hundreds—thousands—of hard little marbles, swarming in their hills like ants.

We realized Bill's cough was not going away. He'd start out of nowhere, or even in his sleep, sitting bolt upright in bed and clasping his throat. Then he'd lean over the side of the bed and hack, deep rattling spasms, and he'd cough and he'd cough till he gagged. On the bad nights he threw up into a garbage pail that never left the bedside.

I finished the critical renovations myself and we left the rest half-done. We could paint the hallway next year. Insulate the attic next year. Pave the driveway next year. Start again next year.

Snow fell. The dandelions withered. Bill withered. He was home most of the winter, sitting in front of the fire with a blanket wrapped around his shoulders, chasing warmth he couldn't quite catch. We tried for Christmas.

I remember picking up my present and hesitating for a moment before I tore the paper off, remembering that first fat ear of corn, recalling how it had felt to pull back the leaves and see the hideous malformed ear within, seething with bugs, stippled all over by moldy growths. I'd had to pause and tell myself there was nothing like that waiting for me within the colourful wrapping.

It was the diamond earrings I'd longed for, and they were perfectly fine, beautiful even. Still, I couldn't quite bring myself to buy Bill the tins of syrup-filled chocolates his family had always had at Christmastime. I noticed that he didn't ask why there weren't any, and that he didn't buy a tin for himself. We skipped the traditional holiday dinner and ordered Chinese takeout.

We made the best of Christmas, and I joined him there next to the fire and we made love beside the Christmas tree, an artificial tree, the same one we'd had in our tiny apartment in the city. The same one Bill had threatened to throw out before we moved. The same one I'd packed anyway in a fit of nostalgia. It went up without question, and it stayed up until January, smelling of dust and plastic but standing straight and tall and strong.

In the dark days of winter Bill came down.

Bill had been the breadwinner in the family; his income covered our necessities, my income purchased our luxuries. It had been a good arrangement. Now, hiring a personal assistant would've cost more money than I made, so I quit my job and stayed home to look after Bill. I trusted that our savings would last us until Bill recovered, told myself that magazines lied and our dreams had never been practical, recited over and over that reality always had warts.

But Bill's not getting any better. His cough echoes hollowly through the upstairs; then a jagged retch chokes him to silence. When the snow was on the ground, that sound sent me into a panic, running upstairs to tend to him. Now it's just background noise. There's nothing I can do for him. Maybe nothing anyone can do.

I'll go to him. Soon. In a moment. But first, I just need a few seconds to breathe.

I open the window for a little fresh air and notice, from the corner of my eye, a patch of brilliant magenta. I hold my breath. My Sweet William is alive. Alive, and blooming, overshadowing the strange dandelions.

My gardening book—the one I'd bought right before the move, the one I'd purchased when I'd been so excited about a house with a garden of my own—had warned me that Sweet William would not flower the first year after planting. I'd laid down the seed in the beds around the yard anyway, and watched green stems grow. Unlike the rest of my garden, the Sweet William had stood tall and strong and brilliant, vibrant green. When everything else went wrong I looked at those beautiful healthy leaves and told myself I could at least do something right.

Between Bill and…other things, I hadn't given the garden any consideration this year. I hadn't even realized the Sweet William was still alive. I hadn't weeded it, watered it, anything. I look at the purple flowers, and smile…and pause.

Choking, heart in my throat, I run for my gardening book. I snatch it off the shelf, crack it open, and return to the window, frantically flipping pages. I fumble for the photo of Sweet William and almost tear the page from the book, but finally I have the book open, its spine pressed to the window pane, a glossy photograph of Sweet William blossoms on the left side, the view of my garden through the screen on the right.

On the left side, immortalized in shiny paper, Sweet William blooms. The photograph shows clusters of ten or so blooms, pure white at the heart, encircled by rich magenta, and turning pale again at the frilly edges of the flower.

I look through the wire mesh screen and begin to cry.

We have Sweet William like we have dandelions. The stalks are too thick, all doubled and tripled up, and there are too many leaves, rolled so tightly they look more like pine needles, sticking out in between the flowers, jagged like a cough. The petals are tattered, as though something's been eating at them. There's a breeze, and it carries to me the sweet smell of flowers and rot, like a breath of embalming fluid.

I clutch my stomach and fear for the baby in my belly.

Mary Pletsch is a glider pilot, toy collector and graduate of the Royal Military College of Canada. She attended Superstars Writing Seminars in 2010 and has since published multiple short stories in a variety of genres including science fiction, horror, and fantasy. Mary lives in New Brunswick with Dylan Blacquiere and their four cats. Visit her online at www.fictorians.com.

Deerborn

by Leslie J. Anderson

When I was five my parents
had my horns removed. They told
their friends that I had fallen
learning to walk. I wore the scabs
like a crown of rubies.

The other children knew. We touched
our foreheads with tiny fingers in salute.

They painted the ragged fences white.
The old farmhouses caught fire.
Jason said he saw the hawks circle
the smoke for three days and nights.

The trees tiptoed in at night,
slid their roots into the charcoal, like fingers
into secret black hair. Their bark was white.
We grew up in uneasy air. We come out wild.

The schools kept us in tights and charcoal shoes.
The schools told us not to run, to line up.

At night we stole our fathers' hunting rifles,
opened bedroom windows
loud as nervous cats, slinking through the forests
ashes up to our ankles.

We built fires together, and ran through the ash
slamming our heads together, striking off sparks
I waited my turn, slid my fingers into the ash—
found something reaching back.

Leslie J. Anderson specializes in urban fantasy, science fiction, and horror short stories and poetry. In her spare time she trains various animals. She has an unhealthy obsession with coffee.

Her collection of poetry, *An Inheritance of Stone,* was recently released form **Alliteration Ink**, and her novel, *The Cricket Prophecies,* was released by **Post Mortem Press**. Her writing has appeared in *Asimov's, Strange Horizons, Daily Science Fiction,* and *Andromeda Spaceways Inflight Magazine,* to name a few.

Her poetry has been nominated for Pushcart and Rhysling Awards.

Burnt Offerings, by Robert Marasco; Valancourt Books, 2015; 218 pgs.

 Marian and Ben Rolf and their son, Danny, have had enough of living in their noisy, cramped, hot New York apartment. Their solution: renting a sprawling mansion in the countryside from elderly sibling owners, Roz and Arnold Allardyce, at a steal of $900 for the entire summer. The one catch: the Rolfs have to bring three square meals to the Allardyce's elderly mother every day. Thinking this a perfect solution, the Rolfs move in, along with Ben's aunt, Elizabeth. Scared yet? Don't be—there are no ghosts wailing in dark corners in the mansion; just like the Rolfs, you can just curl up with this book, kick back, and make yourself quite at home...

In some ways, *Burnt Offerings* is quite an unusual haunted house novel. Although there are plenty of creepy moments that inevitably threaten the sanity of its main characters, there are no half-glimpsed figures or creaking walls to be found inside the mansion. Some readers may be a little disappointed to come out of this haunted house (novel) knowing very little more about the nature of the building than they did going in; like any unstudied force of nature, the mansion works in mysterious ways, with only the effects of its sinister architecture hinting at its carnivorous machinations.

Robert Marasco's style contains flavors of older literary styles, but the occasional (still fairly) contemporary references demand the reader's attention, serving as a reminder that this is very much a tale of a modern family from a modern city going into a very old, very traditional location. Subtleties run rampant throughout, with the bulk of the scares being *suggested*, rather than shown. True, this novel was released after Shirley Jackson's *The Haunting of Hill House* and Richard Matheson *Hell House*, but it's also from *before* the world was introduced to the Overlook Hotel.

The characters seem a bit underdeveloped at times, namely in the most central of the characters, Marian Rolf, who serves as the equivalent of Eleanor from *The Haunting of Hill House* in being both the central protagonist and the ultimate target of the encroaching terrors. However, there seems to be a very deliberate process behind the characters' developments (or lack thereof); Robert Marasco very succinctly kept their personalities just well-enough illustrated that the reader cares to find out what's in store for them, yet saving page space for the rich prose, keeping the storyline taut and the atmosphere pitch-black.

For all its subtleties, *Burnt Offerings* offers up a number of vividly terrifying images to keep the back of your neck acrawl; to divulge them is to spoil the fun of wandering into the mansion's silent halls. All you really need to know is that the deeper you travel, the more you will feel the sense that something is most definitely *not right* about the mansion—and by the time you know it would be best to exit, well…you *do* want to stay and find out what happens to the Rolfs, don't you?

While another 1973 horror novel called *Carrie* grabbed everyone's attention upon its release, this book went almost unnoticed that same year, although there was a brief increase in reception three years later with a now-classic film starring Karen Black and Oliver Reed. Subsequently, *Burnt Offerings* spent far several long decades out of print—but now it has a new home in Valancourt Books, available in both e-book and print form, and with a loving (if lovingly terrified) and informative introduction by Stephen Graham Jones. The mansion is once again open for residence; come in, relax, and don't you worry about Mrs. Allardyce; you'll hardly even know that she's there.

–Barry Lee Dejasu

Exigencies, Edited by Richard Thomas; Darkhouse Press, 2015; 337 pgs.

The New Black was one of the best things I read last year, a startlingly good collection of what the kid's are calling "neo-noir" but what I like to refer to as simply unique dark fiction. *Exigencies* is good enough to be considered a sequel. From the get-go we are punched, pinched, and pummeled into a sense of dread and uncertainty as to how we ought to feel about what we're reading. The stories are great gobs of greasy and grimy dark, they are souls of black being siphoned and spat out even blacker. They stick with you, these stories.

The collection opens with Letitia Trent's "Wilderness," in which a woman is stranded in a rural airport  terminal for mysterious reasons and discovers that people will always be the most horrific of monsters. "Cat Calls," by Rebecca Jones-Howe, shows us what happens when the sexist shoe is on the other foot. "Ceremony of the White Dog," by Kevin Catalano, is a *Gummo* sort of story, seedy and wrong from the first few sentences, but you cannot peel your eyes from the prose even when the most gruesome and depraved events take place.

Nathan Beauchamp's "The Mother" is a strange beast about… well, a strange beast and its brood, while "Figure Eight," by Brendan Detzner, presents the events of a cult and its few members after they begin to experience a crisis of faith. W. P. Johnson's "Searching for Gloria" is a wonderful tale of a killer and his young protégé and their quest for a small girl for a very bad man. David James Keaton is an interesting fellow who writes interesting things in a very interesting manner. With "A Dull Boy" he takes the grown up actor who played Danny Torrance from *The Shining* and supposes what his life must be like now.

These stories offer a fresh voice, although it's a raspy shadow-choked voice, that speaks to a place where the heart hides all the terrible things we think. It touches those raw and sore spots under our eyelids where we see those vile things we lack the courage to go through with. *Exigencies* is the soundtrack to play when you finally snap, when that Louisville Slugger in your hands isn't for playing a game with friends but a means to end the sound-making creatures that surround you, steal your air, and just don't understand.

–John Boden

Qualia Nous, Edited by Michael Bailey; Written Backwards Press, 2014; 446 pgs.

Michael Bailey and his publishing house, Written Backwards, are a force to reckon with. They don't pump out a large volume of work, usually an anthology a year and maybe another release or two. But what they release is stunning. Beautiful to behold and amazing to read. This collection is certainly no exception, as *Qualia Nous* is quite an achievement and a fine example of what can happen when you open the doors a little and ask for a literary blend of science fiction and horror.

The hefty volume opens with a reprint from the master, Stephen King. "The Jaunt" first appeared in his *Skeleton Crew* collection almost thirty years ago. It is still a wonderfully frightening and gleefully disturbing slice of modern sci-fi. Usman T. Malik gives us a spell-binding story in "The Vaporization Enthalpy of a Peculiar Pakistani Family," an incredible story that chronicles a family struggle and the heartbreaking culmination of it all. Erik T. Johnson's "The Angel Chaser" is exactly as the title suggests but with a gritty horizon that haunts and hypnotizes.

"Second Chance," by John R. Little, is an aching story about loss and grief and the lengths a man will go to recapture what he lost. "The Neighborhood Has Barbeque," by Max Booth III, is a slightly lighthearted look at an automaton world where what we've created is what we become. Erin Kemper's "Night Guard" is a brilliant and somewhat paranoid exercise in futuristic home protection. In "Voyeur," John Everson gives us a strange tale of a long forgotten machine that likes to watch and learn from what it sees. "Good and Faithful Servant," by Thomas F. Monteleone, is a sharp story about following orders—or not. Mason Ian Bundshuch has in "Breathe You in Me" a jaw-dropper of a tale about death and rebirth and an organic evolution of sorts.

Gary A. Braunbeck ushers us out with his tale, "No Fixed Address." Braunbeck always manages to break my heart and I somehow thought, given the premise of this collection, maybe I'd escape that this time—but I was wrong. His story parallels a quest from millions of years ago with events in present day...and to say more would be a crime. Just read it.

Michael Bailey has an amazing eye for a great story. I mean, one look at his contributing authors and then one read of a finished anthology, and you'll know why all the big names clamor to be included. You'll know why he and his collections are nominated for numerous awards. He does not fuck around. It is all about the quality of the writing and the man know what's good. There are over thirty stories in this book, some good, some great, and others amazing. All of them worth reading.

–John Boden

Fungi, Edited by Silvia Moreno-Garcia and Orrin Grey; Innsmouth Free Press, 2012; 288 pgs.

 In the introduction to this anthology, the editors mention William Hope Hodgson's short story "The Voice of the Night" as being *the* seminal fungal horror story. This, coupled with an impressive roster of guest talents that include the likes of John Langan, Laird Barron, Paul Tremblay, Simon Strantzas, Nick Mamatas, and Jeff VanderMeer, Orrin Grey and Silvia Moreno-Garcia's *Fungi* certainly sounds like a horror anthology; yet much like a thematic organism that isn't quite a plant nor an animal, the contents herein are not all quite one genre or another. Science

fiction, fantasy, postmodern satire and more are only a few of the creative genres at work here.

(Reviewer's Note: I highly recommend that you cough up the extra cash to acquire the hardcover edition of this book, because not only does it have a few neat Mike Mignola-esque illustrations that aren't included in the paperback or e-book versions, it has a total of *three* short stories that aren't otherwise available! Why the publisher would do such a thing, or why the editors would agree to it, is *almost* beyond my understanding, although a word that starts with "g" and rhymes with "bleed" comes to mind.)

Make no mistake about it: if you're looking for horror, this book has plenty of it. John Langan's nightmarish "Hyphae" builds its unnerving suspense with every step the protagonist takes into his father's house. H.P. Lovecraft would have been proud of Daniel Mills's "Dust from a Dark Flower," an excellent, old-fashioned period piece of gothic terror, as well as Kristopher Resz's slow-burn of eerie beauty, "The Pilgrims of Parthen." Simon Strantzas brings on the deeply unsettling with his nightmarish "Go Home Again," and of course a memorable favorite was Laird Barron's prismatic, hallucinatory "Gamma."

If science fiction, fantasy, or some kind of blend of the two is what you're seeking, then there's plenty of it to be found here. Camille Alexa's "His Sweet Truffle of a Girl" was a delightfully strange underwater adventure-fantasy, whereas Andrew Penn Romine's "Last Bloom on the Sage" was the best fungal western action-adventure you'll ever read (and more likely, the *only* one). Lavie Tidhar recounts the alternate history of a world populated by sentient cybes in "The White Hands." With "Corpse Mouth and Nose Spore," Jeff VanderMeer returns to his signature world of Ambergris (featured in his novels *City of Saints and Madmen*, *Shriek: An Afterward*, and *Finch*) to tell an unsettling tale of a detective's strange discovery. And E. Catherine Tobler's "New Feet Within My Garden Go," one of the three hardcover-only stories, is a twisted fantasy that is by turns mysteriously alluring, grotesquely engaging, and morbidly beautiful.

There are other stories that are far less easy to classify. Paul Tremblay's excellent "Our Stories Will Live Forever" starts out as an unnerving plane ride, only to turn into something epically tragic and surreal. Nick Mamatas tells a short, aloof, and ever-so-gently weird urban tale in "The Shaft Through the Middle of It All," and Jane Hertenstein's "Wild Mushrooms" was a heartbreaking, nostalgic tale of a family.

Not all of the stories worked for me, and at times I knew that I was just not the right target audience; Mollly Tanzer and Jesse Bullington's "Tubby McMungus, Fat from Fungus" is a perfect example of this, as is Ann K. Schwader's poem "Cordyceps Zombii." W.H. Pugmire's "Midnight Mushrumps" was a bit pastiche and overdone (if an interesting companion piece to Oliver Wetter's cover illustration). The florid prose of A.C. Wise's "Where Dead Men Go to Dream" was just too "pretty" for me. Julio Toro San Martin's "A Monster in the Midst" was a fun-enough

seafaring adventure, but its thumbing-of-the-nose twist ending was kind of annoying. And while the tongue-in-cheek humor of Polenth Blake's "Letters to a Fungus" was lost on me, Richard Gavin's "Goatsbride" felt a bit out of place in the anthology with its brief, passing mention of fungi.

Rounding out *Fungi* is a list of further "fungal fiction" that readers may enjoy, some of which I highly approve, namely the short stories by Brian Lumley, T.E.D. Klein, H.P. Lovecraft, and Stephen King. This list also includes various movies and even TV episodes (both of which feature a few adaptations of the suggested fiction), and is a fun addition to the book.

All in all, *Fungi* is a somewhat uneven anthology, but still pretty good, and like the organism it's named after, it's truly unique. As far as I can tell, there has not yet been a name given to this particular niche/subgenre, so here's to dubbing it "sporepunk."

–Barry Lee Dejasu

***Shadows Over Main Street*, Edited by Doug Murano and D. Alexander Ward; Hazardous Press, 2015; 280 pgs.**

If the current glut of anthologies is any indication, Lovecraftian horror is the flavor du jour. If I'm being honest, I'm beginning to grow as weary of them as I did with anything zombie-related a few years back. But I'm a trooper and so I keep on reading...

The original idea behind this collection was to be a mashup of

Lovecraftian themes but setting the diabolical goings on in the fictional burg of Mayberry. Someone in power over the rights of that anemic small town's name said, "No," and so a slight gear shift was enacted. What we have is basically the same damn thing, but with each small town setting being its own unique place rather than that place kept safe by Andy Griffth and Don Knotts. Small-town horror with a Lovecraftian bite.

With a foreword by one of the greatest writers of somewhat-Lovecraftian horror, Ramsey Campbell,  we know this tome means business. Tentacular business. We open with "The 21st Century Shadow," by Stephanie M Wytovich, a page and a half of razor-sharp prose that stands as a promise of the dark things to come. Nick Mamatas gives us the second tale with a title that I cannot type, but can copy and paste from the Internet—"Χταπόδι Σαλάτα." It is a strangely comic story of culinary discord and elder gods. Kevin Lucia's "The Black Pyramid" is a greatly old-school tale about a preacher longing to recapture his flock and the glory due him and the strange object that helps him in his quest.

Chesya Burke's "Mountaintown" is a powerful tale of judgment and debts, all wrapped in a deliciously Appalachian setting. James Chambers gives us a heaping helping of cursed clams in "Odd Quahogs." Tim Curran's "The Thing with a Thousand Legs" is pure nightmare fuel. Aaron Polson's

"Undergrounders" is a ghoulish tale of lineage and duty. Richard Thomas's "White Picket Fences" allows us a glimpse into what horrors can lurk behind even the sweetest of little old ladies. Once again, Gary A. Braunbeck knocks it over the fence with his gripping noir meets Lovecraft-at-the-Carny tale "The Friendless Bodies of Unburied Men."

Josh Malerman, whose novel *Bird Box* was one of the best things I've read this year, gives us "A Fiddlehead Party on Carpenter's Farm," a strangely unsettling tale of new neighbors. Nearing the end is Jay Wilburn's "Boss Cthulu," which is a slightly zany tale about two good ol' boys and their struggles with loyalty when the Great Ones show themselves.

Shadows Over Main Street is a solid anthology, crammed full of well-written and entertaining tales of creatures fishy and/or slithery, tentacles and sucker-mouths. Not everyone is a grabber, but all are good and fun. It is a collection that has a lot of heart, a success in crafting a wonderful book that will stand as an example of new-millennium Lovecraftian horror.

–John Boden

A Head Full of Ghosts, by Paul Tremblay; William Morrow, 2015; 304pgs.

With every novel, short story, collaboration, and contribution he's put out over the past decade, Paul Tremblay has proven himself again and again to be a force to be reckoned with. Be it a spin on the mystery genre featuring the narcoleptic detective of *The Little Sleep* and *No Sleep Till Wonderland*, or a genre-blending socio-fantastical world in *Swallowing a Donkey's Eye*, Tremblay always knows how to tell a startlingly original and deeply moving tale, and with *A Head Full of Ghosts* (published by none other than William Morrow), the mainstream is going to get a grand introduction to his magic.

To describe this novel's plot is tricky, not so much for fear of spoiling 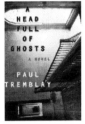 the story as for the complexity of its narrative. At its heart, it takes place in the early twenty-first century household of the Barrett family, who are under a lot of stress: the older of the two daughters, Marjorie, is showing signs of what may well be a demonic possession. Subsequently, the Barretts seek the services of not only a priest, but a film crew—for their tale is being turned into a reality TV series, called *The Possession*.

Now, take that storyline and fold it into this one: key episodes of *The Possession* are being reviewed by a present-day blogger, elevating that narrative into postmodern territory. The blogger brings up the coincidence of Marjorie Barrett's apparent demonic possession in a day and age ruled by films such as *The Exorcist* and the *Paranormal Activity* franchise, and how so many of the strange activities at work in the TV show have many similarities to not just the aforementioned and related movies, but to a variety of written fiction.

But wait! There's more! Framing both of these narratives is present-day Merry, no longer the 8-year-old girl at the time of *The Possession*'s shooting, but now a 23-year-old woman relating her story to a bestselling author with the hopes of casting her own light on the events surrounding her sister's possession.

This Russian nesting dolls-like narrative structure (most classically used in *Frankenstein*) has earned a few early comparisons to Mark Z. Danielewski's *House of Leaves*, which is fair to an extent, although that book takes a far more instrumental direction, using its aesthetic as part of the storytelling. Instead, *A Head Full of Ghosts* embraces a more straightforward narrative-within-a-narrative approach, keeping its prismatic tale a bit more organic in feeling. (It is also reminiscent, in both subject matter and overall narrative approach, of Caitlín R. Kiernan's novel *The Drowning Girl*, as well as Joe Hill's novella "Voluntary Committal," from his collection *20th Century Ghosts*, both of which would make excellent companion pieces to this one.)

With the blog entry narrative, Tremblay shows that not only is he acutely aware of all the possession/exorcism fiction and films that have come before this, he very smartly (and lovingly) *embraces* them, rather than competing against them. This is a novel that both deconstructs the possession tale as well as breathes new life into a very worn subgenre.

Besides being a collective homage to the possession/exorcism tale, this novel makes a number of literary winks to other works and authors, most notably T.E.D. Klein, Charlotte

Perkins Gilman, H.P. Lovecraft, and even the aforementioned *House of Leaves*. (There are even a few characters in this novel named after very real people, but I won't spoil the fun.)

The characters themselves are richly illustrated, warts and all. Although the spotlight is on Merry, Marjorie, and their parents, *every* character gets his or her own distinct personality. The visiting holy men and the film crew are far from the trope-heavy symbols of hope and faith; they are instead every bit as imperfect and flawed as the Barretts, and are often even more clueless as to what's really going on and what to do than the poor family themselves.

A Head Full of Ghosts is very much a tale of horror, and Tremblay knows how to unnerve the hell out of the reader. He masterfully laces threads of tension into nearly every scene, lulling you into the comfort of his narrative so that by the time the terror steps forth from the shadows of implication and onto the page before you, you're too scared to do anything but read on. There were a few times I was reading the book with a hand clamped over my mouth, eyes wide, afraid to even let my breath out, and there are some afterimages that will not be leaving my mind's eye anytime soon. Whether or not you're a fan of the horror genre, this is one truly unsettling book.

So in the end, does it matter *what* is "really going on" in this tale? Not really, but what *does* matter is how the strange events affected everyone in young Merry's life, and how they in turn had ultimately affected *her*, leaving her with her own "head full of ghosts." Besides the frequent moments of paranoia, terror, and uncertainty, there are conversations, arguments, and tearful solitudes; all very real things that might happen during a traumatic time, and for the Barrett family, there's no shortage of trauma at work with Marjorie's alleged possession.

Ultimately, the masterful touch that makes this novel so damn effective is just how heart-wrenchingly *sad* it is. True, many of the best scary movies and books portray characters' families, sanity, and lives crumbling around the chaos of terror, but what sets this novel apart from the majority of its peers is that Tremblay deftly delivers the scares with an unflinching, richly detailed look at their effects upon the characters, making it as heartbreaking as it is horrifying.

This will easily be remembered as one of the most powerfully disquieting and deeply unsettling novels in recent years, and may mark something of a turning point in the mainstream horror genre. Take a look inside *A Head Full of Ghosts*, and see what you find there.

—Barry Lee Dejasu

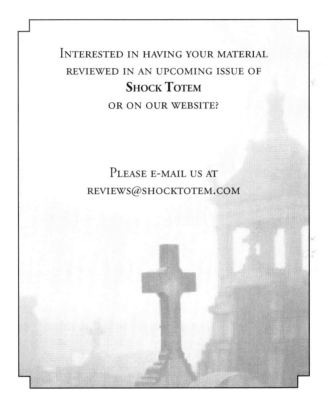

Interested in having your material
reviewed in an upcoming issue of
Shock Totem
or on our website?

Please e-mail us at
reviews@shocktotem.com

THERE'S A TONGUE IN THE DRAIN

by Roger Lovelace

Yllie left her shoes in the winter garden and ran blue-foot through the snow, stopping over the drain grate. A tongue slipped out from under the grate and licked the snow sticking to her feet. It tickled. She was still laughing when she rushed into the house. Mother was hammering a wad of dough into submission on the oak slab. "Why can't you wipe your feet like a normal girl?"

"Sorry, Madda." She smelled the apples roasting over the fire. A large, charred hand, reaching down from the chimney, turned the spit, slowly and with conviction. Yllie smacked her lips. The arm held out the spit; she slid an apple from the metal prong and bit into it.

"Where are your shoes?" Her mother continued to pound the dough like a crazed pugilist, occasionally stopping to wipe the sweat from her face with the hem of her apron.

"In the garden." She took another bite of the apple. "I like it when Bruno licks my feet."

"You and that grate will end up no good, Yllie. Next time you leave your shoes on, or I'll switch you good."

Yllie sat at the window, chewing and pouting, looking out toward the forest, wanting to see Fa emerge from the woods. He and the other men were helping young Josh bury a giant's Larva under the floorboards of his wedding house.

"Madda?"

"Yes."

When you and Fadda got married did the men help him bury Bruno?"

"Of course, dear. And some day when you get married, Fadda will help your man build a fine house with a Larva of your own."

"I don't want a Larva of my own. I want Bruno."

Madda laughed and wiped the apple juice from Yllie's chin.

Yllie tossed the apple core into the floor dump and under the boards; Bruno chewed the sweet. "Bruno loves me," Yllie said.

"Dear daughter, a house giant can't love." Madda wrinkled her brow, clearly searching for the right words for her strange daughter with her strange ideas. "It's a tool. It works for us, hoping to escape from the earth. The tongue would run away if there wasn't a grate, and then who would keep our stoop clean? If it wasn't chained to the chimney, Bruno's arm would crawl up the flue with the smoke and then who would turn the spit and stir the pot?"

Yllie stopped listening and returned to looking out of the window. *Madda doesn't know anything. Bruno does love me!*

~

In her small loft, Yllie was cleaning Bruno's ear, which hung patiently from the wall. She made candles with the wax. She sang into the ear as she swabbed the recesses with a large cloth. Her tiny round window opened above the front door. The moon was out and she glanced down to see Bruno's tongue tasting the cold night sky through the grate. Fa had not returned yet and the house was quiet.

She peeked over the edge of the loft and saw Madda slowly rocking in her chair, intent on her sewing. While she worked, a large foot reached up through the tiny cellar door and rubbed the back of her neck. Madda quit sewing and blew the candle out. Soft moans reached Yllie, who, vaguely troubled, crept back to bed and went to sleep. When she woke up the next morning she smelled sausage cooking, and Fadda's voice drifting up with it. Yllie bounded from bed and hurried down the ladder.

"Fa!" She rushed to him and he captured her in his bearish arms. He smelled like coffee and tobacco and his beard tickled her face. She tugged at it and he pretended to howl in pain.

"Madda tells me you've been letting the grate lick your bare feet?"

"What's wrong with that, Fa?" Her parents glanced at each other, and looked at Bruno's curious eye hovering over them, dangling at the end of a fleshy string that disappeared into a crack in the floor. Fa punched Bruno's eye, which floated into the corner. Fa took his boots off, revealing large furry feet. He walked to the front door and went out. Madda had closed her eyes and was humming softly, massaged by six calloused toes. Yllie sneaked outside.

Fadda stood on the grate and the tongue flew out to explore his feet. Yllie watched Fadda's face contorting into an expression she'd never seen. There was something horrible about what the grate was doing to Fa.

Yllie couldn't move. The tongue's happy licking shouldn't look like that. It didn't look like that when she stood on the grate. She slipped back into the house.

Madda opened her eyes. "Bruno licks everyone's feet. It's what he does."

Yllie looked up at Madda. "Bruno's just part of our house?" Yllie glanced out of the window. Fadda continued standing on the grate, framed by the window casement and winter behind him. The tongue licked his feet fast and faster.

"When you have a house of your own with a Larva buried beneath, you will understand."

"When can I get a house of my own?"

Her mother smiled.

Fadda came in from the cold and warmed his feet by the fire. "Tell her, Myrtle."

Madda nodded. "You will live in Josh's house. He will be your husband and his house will be yours. The Larva will lick your feet whenever you want. That's for grownups."

"I don't want to grow up." Yllie knuckled away tears from the corners of her eyes, and cried, "This licking thing is yuck!"

Later, as she lay in her bed, Yllie remembered the raspy, wet touch on the soles of her feet, the wonderful tickling, the soft suckling on her toes, and she couldn't help but wonder.

Roger Lovelace calls the Tennessee Valley home, and currently lives in Athens, Alabama. He enjoys the slow pace but not the humidity. Always an avid reader, he has recently turned to writing, concentrating primarily on short stories and flash fiction. He shares his home with a Chiweenie dog, Dixie and a cat. It gets quirky sometimes.

WASPS

by Thana Niveau

*M*urderer!"

The voice of pure rage is scary enough from grown-ups. From another kid it's bone-chilling. The little girl's voice was shrill and choked with anguish and I almost fell off my bike when I first heard it. Over and over she screamed it at the top of her lungs.

"Murderer!"

I tried to ignore it and ride on, but her voice was in my head and it refused to go away, even when she paused for breath. I kept thinking any minute she'd stop, but the pain in her voice told me she would go on as long as it took. And besides, I was curious.

It wasn't hard to find her and by the time I did, a hoarse old man's voice yelled for her to shut up. It only made her scream louder.

I climbed over the chain link fence into an empty lot. The foundation of a demolished house sprawled over the weed-infested ground like the chalk outline of a murder victim. A girl my age was standing at its edge, clutching the limp body of a huge orange cat. She wore a torn black T-shirt thin as tissue and shorts that were way too big. I instantly pegged both as hand-me-downs from some older sibling. She was barefoot, her feet and legs streaked with mud. Definitely what my parents would call "poor white trash."

Something about her both frightened and fascinated me and I approached her as I might a wild animal. "Hey," I said softly.

She whirled with the cat in her arms, a frenzied look in her eyes.

I took a step back, startled. "It's okay," I whispered. "What happened?"

She eyed me for a moment as though sizing me up. Then she nodded towards the back of the house adjacent to the empty lot. "That old man," she said. "Fucking psycho!" She spat in his direction.

I had never heard anyone my age use the F word before and I felt a surge of awe. I would never have had the guts to scream and curse at anyone, especially not some crazy old man I thought had killed my cat.

"His name is Ivan," she said quietly, tears spilling from her eyes. She scrubbed them away with a grimy fist, transferring the heavy cat to one arm. His head lolled and fixed me with a dull, glassy stare that made me shudder. She tried to scream once more, but her voice caught in her throat and she surrendered to her tears.

I could never stand to see anyone or anything in pain and my heart ached for her. I wanted to reassure her, to tell her it would be okay. But I was afraid to get too close to her. I was afraid of the cat she clung to with no aversion to its death.

"What did he do?" I asked at last.

"He said he was going to make me get rid of Ivan because he kept climbing in his attic." As she spoke she caressed the cat's lifeless fur, making its head sway like a stone in a sock. "So he killed him."

I winced, not wanting to know the details. Earlier that year, my own beloved cat, Domino, had run away. I put up flyers with his picture, desperately hoping he would turn up. A few days later a neighbor came by and said he thought he'd found my cat. My heart sank at the sympathetic tone in his voice. It told me everything. It was a long walk down the street to his house. Black and white tufts of fur led the way into his garden like nine discarded lives. Domino's open-mouthed, vacant face haunted me for weeks, and I woke from nightmares full of yowling and hissing cats.

Domino was the first dead thing I ever saw. Ivan was the second.

"Let's bury him," I said.

The girl locked steady eyes on mine and stared at me for a long time. Then she nodded. I had the weird sense that I had passed some kind of test.

The sky was dark, threatening to drench us with rain as we scouted broken bottles to use as spades. We didn't talk much while we dug but she told me her name was Mitzie. It was a strange, scratchy sort of name, but it seemed to fit her.

We couldn't make the hole very deep but we did our best. When we were done Mitzie lifted her arms like a priestess and bowed her head over the grave to say a few words. There was something of a rehearsed quality to it all and I began to suspect it wasn't the first funeral she'd presided over.

When the rain began to fall, Mitzie didn't move, so I didn't either. I was mesmerized by her. She was a force, this girl. She felt things so intensely and it seemed a kind of honor to be allowed to share in her grief.

I stood there with her in the cold rain, perversely enjoying the misery of it as I waited for her to finish speaking. Then I asked her meekly if I could be her friend.

The first night we spent together, Mitzie wanted us to prick our fingers and share our blood like she'd seen in a movie, but I was too afraid of the pain. Mitzie looked stunned, as though I'd said something in another language.

"What do you mean you're afraid?" she asked, staring at the sewing needle she was going to use.

I shrank back as she poised it over her hand, and then pressed it into the tip of her little finger. She didn't even do it fast. She took her time and pushed it in slowly, like she was enjoying it. Blood welled from the puncture and she held the dripping needle out to me.

"Your turn."

"No way! I can't do that!"

"Then how are we gonna be blood-sisters? You have to make a sacrifice."

I tried to think of alternatives, but Mitzie's suggestions—knife, razor—were even scarier than the needle. In desperation I tried scraping my hands against the icicles in her parents' empty freezer. I'd once cut myself like that by accident, but it wouldn't work when I tried to do it deliberately.

Impatient with my squeamishness, Mitzie finally grabbed my hand and jabbed the needle into my finger.

"Ow!"

"Don't be such a baby!" She laughed, pressing my bloody finger to hers. "Now you're a part of me."

When it was done she licked both our fingers. My stomach fluttered with unease.

I was too naive to understand the dark side to a fascination with blood. Instead, I simply admired her bravery. And even though I was always a little afraid of her, she made me feel special. I was someone she wanted with her forever.

"Come on, let's go play in the funhouse!"

Mitzie raced off then, leaving me on my own. It was part of the game, following her in so she could jump out and scare me. Just another part of my mysterious role in her life.

The funhouse was what she called the shack in the weed-choked field behind her house. It was a pile of rotting timber that any parents but hers would have torn down years ago. She didn't know who had built it but her grandfather had lived and died in it. Mitzie adored the place and she cherished the memory of a man she had barely known, though I had to wonder what kind of man would be banished to a shack behind the real house.

She loved to wait behind the door and pounce on me when I came in, covering my eyes with her hands and leading me blindly around the room. I had to trust her to steer me around the holes in the floor and the drips from above. One time she made me close my eyes while she put something in my hand. I thought it was a rock, but when she finally let me look I realised it was the skull of a bird. I dropped it in fright and brushed my hand on my jeans. Mitzie just laughed, her eyes gleaming.

It was one of the hottest summers on record. Even so, we spent most of our time outside. My parents didn't want "that trashy girl" in their house, but we didn't mind our exile. Her field contained just enough trees to count as a forest, and we created our own little world out there. We pretended to be witches, making potions and casting spells we were sure would come true if we only wished hard enough. Instead of animals we sacrificed locks of hair or fingernails. Occasionally a bug if Mitzie insisted on something living.

Before I met her I would never have dreamed of sneaking out of my house at night. Now I thought nothing of slipping out through my window with only the light of the moon to guide me. The spirits of the forest were there, Mitzie said, watching over us. They would protect us.

But nature isn't always kind, as I soon found out.

I was so excited that day. I had finally climbed my parents' huge magnolia tree all the way to the top, a feat I never thought I would manage. I cheered and shouted down at Mitzie, exuberant in my triumph. I felt like I'd scaled a mountain.

And then I heard it.

There was no mistaking the sound – the telltale buzzing that surrounded me like a cloud. I wasn't alone up there. As the sickening realization set in, I stared into the swirling black and yellow vortex for several slow-motion moments. Then the wasps began to attack.

I screamed, waving my arms at them and almost losing my balance. The hard ground and a broken leg seemed a small price to pay for escaping, but some rational part of me refused to let me jump. I was too high up and, even in my hysteria, I knew that the fall could kill me. So I started climbing down. And they started stinging.

I looked down as I climbed, searching frantically for Mitzie, hoping she would save me somehow. Instead I saw her running away. My heart twisted, but the wrenching pain was nothing compared to the nightmare of the wasps.

They were everywhere, filling the sky like smoke. I could barely see. I flailed at them, their hard little bodies knocking against my hands and veering dizzily away, only to circle back with renewed fury once they'd regained their balance. Others clung to me – my skin, my clothes, my hair. One flew right into my face and my senses were so heightened that I actually felt its wing brush my eye as it tried to blind me with its evil stinger. I heard my voice as though from miles away. Screaming, screaming, screaming.

I slipped on the branches as I scrambled to get down, trying desperately not to lose my grip and fall. My palms were slick with blood, but the only pain I felt was the terrible stinging. I thought of witches burned at the stake, flames licking all around them, charring their flesh. Excruciating. Inescapable. I was drowning in fire. Through the terror and the pain came a final coherent thought: I'm going to die.

And then suddenly the world was full of water. I cried out at the shock of it, bewildered by the cold wet blast. It was raining! No, that was impossible. But some of the wasps had been washed away and I could see again. I was soaked to the skin before I realised that the icy spray was coming from below me, from the base of the tree. Mitzie hadn't abandoned me after all.

The swarm broke apart like confetti thrown to the wind, powerless against the onslaught of water. I was able to climb faster now and when I made it down to the first fork in the trunk I jumped, landing hard in the wet grass.

Mitzie ran to me, still spraying me with the garden hose. I couldn't do anything but cower on the ground, trembling, sobbing, swiping at the endless pain. Mitzie peeled away a few wasps that were still tangled in my hair and I howled as another one stung my lower back. It had crawled inside my shirt. With renewed panic I started tearing off my clothes.

"You're okay, you're okay," Mitzie said firmly, holding me still and patting me down as though searching for weapons. "They're gone."

It took me a long time to believe that. Even once I was safe inside the house,

I could still feel their jagged little legs crawling on my arms, my face, the back of my neck. Violent shudders racked my body and I kept running my hands through my hair, convinced that some were still hiding in there. And the buzzing. I didn't think I would ever stop hearing it. If Mitzie hadn't been there...

More than a dozen of the evil things had stung me. The worst one was just below my left eyebrow and it swelled into what looked like a black eye. Mitzie thought that was cool. But then, she would.

"I've never seen anyone look so scared," she said. She was breathless with exhilaration.

My parents were horrified when they saw what had happened and, I suspect, not a little disappointed that they couldn't somehow blame Mitzie for it. I told them again and again that she had saved my life and they grudgingly thanked her and said she could play inside with me until I recovered.

It took a few days for the swelling to go down enough for me to feel halfway normal again, but even though Mitzie was welcome inside now, it wasn't the same. We couldn't lose ourselves there the way we could in the forest or the funhouse. Mixing potions from household ingredients felt like a cheat after seeking out exotic roots and mushrooms in the field, and we missed the flowers, the birds, and the squirrels. We were like wild animals in a zoo, caged when we should be running free.

But even though I felt trapped, I was terrified of venturing back outside. My dad promised he'd hired an exterminator to kill the wasps and destroy the nest and Mitzie confirmed that she'd seen it. They were all dead, she assured me. Hundreds of them. The nest was the size of a basketball.

It didn't matter. In my mind they were still there, buzzing, stinging, circling and coming back. They weren't like bees, which could only sting once. A bee sting was a suicide mission. Wasps could hurt you forever.

Mitzie was patient with me but after the first two weeks she couldn't hide her frustration any longer. I felt awful, like I was letting her down. She'd saved my life and in return I was depriving her of our magic world. My parents were civil to her but she knew she wasn't wanted. The forest was the only place to which she could escape, and only with me.

"You'll be safe in the funhouse," she promised. "Nothing can get in there."

But the old shack was full of holes and open to the elements. There were always ladybirds and moths inside so why couldn't there be wasps too?

I *wanted* to go outside. I missed our games as much as she did, even the ones where she scared me. But every time I tried to set foot outside the house, my heart would start hammering and I would gasp for breath like a drowning person. Days and then weeks passed like that and gradually the precious summer melted away.

Eventually Mitzie stopped coming over to see me. I looked for her through the window and I even opened the front door sometimes, hoping to see her outside. But she just wasn't there.

The day before, she'd told me a weird bit of news. The old man who'd had it in for Ivan was dead. Some kind of allergic reaction. He never left the hospital. Something about that felt wrong, but I didn't really give it much thought. I was too upset about having wasted the end of our summer. And then Mitzie was gone and I couldn't think of anything but how I had lost my best friend.

I cried myself to sleep every night after that. I felt the way I had when Domino had run away—bereft and helpless. This time she really had left me behind. My parents tried to hide their relief and it only made me feel more heartbroken. The wasps had taken her from me.

When school started in the fall I had no choice but to leave the house. And by then it wasn't so bad. The terror had faded to a manageable level in my head and I found myself thinking about the attack less and less. I looked for Mitzie at school but she wasn't there. I guessed she might have gone to a different school, but then I had to wonder if perhaps she didn't go to school at all.

A couple of times I went by her house but I didn't have the courage to knock. It didn't look like anyone was living there. Maybe her family had moved away. The thought didn't fill me with the grief it once would have.

Time passed and I made new friends, as kids do. The emotional scars never went away entirely but they did fade. Christmas came and went, then Easter. At last it was June. The final bell rang at school and I was free again for another summer. I raced home and let myself in, not knowing how I would spend the rest of the glorious day, but thrilled beyond all reason just to be free. School was out! I opened the door to my room and froze. There was a note taped outside my bedroom window.

I have a surprise for you, it said. *But you have to come see it.* It was signed simply, "M."

And just like that I was back in time, back in last year's summer. Back with Mitzie.

I knew exactly where she wanted me to go. I also knew that there was no question that I *would* go.

My hands shook with nervous anticipation as I pushed open the creaky door of the funhouse and it was as though the intervening year had never happened. Mitzie stepped out from behind the door and put her hands over my eyes, just as she had done so many times before. And even though I'd been expecting it, I jumped and gave a little cry. Her skin was cool but her touch felt strange. I couldn't help but wonder how much she had changed, and what the time apart had done to her.

Without a word she led me inside. The funhouse felt charged with unnatural energy, as though all the warped and mouldy boards were humming with electricity. After a few steps, she stopped and guided me to the floor, where I sat cross-legged. She didn't have to tell me to keep my eyes closed. I listened to her footsteps as she moved around to stand in front of me. At last she said I could look.

I blinked my eyes open and saw Mitzie for the first time in a year. Her hair was a little longer, a little stringier, but it was the same girl. Her hands were clasped in eager anticipation as she smiled down at whatever her "surprise" was. There was something odd about, her but I couldn't pinpoint exactly what it was. And once I dropped my gaze to the floor and saw what was in front of me, I forgot all about Mitzie.

Panic mushroomed from my heart and I scrambled backward like a cartoon character on a wet ramp, my rear hitting the wooden floor more than once before I found my feet.

Confusion and amusement danced in Mitzie's eyes and then she reached for me. "Hey, it's okay—"

"It's a wasp!" My old wounds awakened like fireworks in response to the angry thing buzzing less than two feet from me. I felt consumed by flames.

"No, wait!" She grabbed my arm and I resisted, struggling against her, lost in the blossoming memory of that awful day in the tree.

"Look at it!"

At last came the gentle touch of reason as I saw what she wanted me to see. The wasp couldn't hurt me. It was quite helpless. Slowly, I turned to look at Mitzie.

"See?" she said. "I told you. You're safe." Then, at my confusion: "I did it for you."

Slowly, very slowly, the panic faded to fear, then revulsion, and finally horror as I saw what she had done. The hideous buzzing thing was missing a wing, the other vibrating like a tiny propeller. Its long alien legs were walking in a meandering, out-of-step cadence in the air and its gleaming black and yellow body was turning, rotating, unable to move. Mitzie had pinned it to the floor.

She bounced over to it, grinning, clearly pleased and proud of what she had done. I couldn't speak. I was transfixed.

After a while Mitzie looked back up at me, her eyes narrowing. "I did it for you," she said again, and this time her voice contained a note of resentment at my ingratitude.

"Thank you" was all I could manage, and that in a dry heave of a whisper.

"I told you" Now she was speaking to her captive. "No one hurts my friends and lives." I hadn't seen her face so grim since Ivan's funeral, and now it was blended with unashamed sadism.

She reached out and took the wasp's remaining wing between expert fingers. Her eyes gleamed at me and then at her victim as she pulled the wing from its socket. It was so deliberate I could almost hear the miniature fleshy rip as it came loose. The wasp buzzed in fury, its body vibrating faster and more frantically. And although there was no creature in the world that could have terrified me more, the suffering of Mitzie's prisoner tore something in my mind.

I had poured salt on a slug once to see what would happen and I watched with mounting nausea as it writhed in slow motion, its moist form disintegrating under the salt. I didn't understand how something so repugnant could communicate pain or inspire such pity, but I was sick with guilt and I poured even more salt over it, trying to speed its merciful death. But that only seemed to make it suffer all the more.

Mitzie was oblivious to my distress as she reached for something else to pluck. This time she took hold of one of its legs. It was as though I were watching the scene through a high-powered lens, every hideous detail of the wasp's mutilated body vivid and crystal clear. The creature jumped and twitched, trying desperately to turn its body, to aim the vicious barb of its stinger at her.

Mitzie laughed and used her other hand to hold it steady and I realized what had been so odd about her touch. The little finger of her left hand was missing.

"Oh my god," I breathed, "Mitzie, what happened to your hand?"

"Hmm?" She looked at me, then down at her hand. She wiggled the remaining fingers and smiled. It was a terrible smile, full of madness and cruelty. And as I watched she pressed her fingertips down hard on the wasp, smearing it into a pale yellow paste against the floor.

My stomach lurched and I clawed for the door behind me. I managed to stumble into the tall grass, but I crumpled to my knees before I had gone ten steps. When I finally looked back through the open doorway, Mitzie was licking her fingers.

I didn't remember running home but I found myself back in my bedroom, drenched in sweat, my sides aching from exertion. I was convinced I could hear something buzzing and I did the deep breathing exercises my dad had taught me the year before. Inhale slowly. Hold. Count to five. Exhale slowly. Again. It calmed my racing heart but it didn't erase the images from my mind. If I closed my eyes I saw Mitzie's mad grin, her ruined hand, her mutilated victim.

I laid awake for hours that night, unable to purge the memory of Mitzie's "surprise." That she thought it was some kind of gift for me was the worst part. Had she honestly believed I'd be happy about what she'd done? Maybe she'd even expected me to join in.

My thoughts led me into all sorts of unpleasant places. I thought of the day I had first met her, the way she had clung to her dead cat and cursed the old man. I thought of our days in the forest. Mostly I thought of the funhouse and the dark games Mitzie had always liked to play...

When I finally slept, my dreams were haunted by wasps. I felt them crawling over me, creeping inside my pajamas, exploring my skin. They crawled inside my mouth, my ears, my eyes. Several times I jolted awake, brushing frantically at myself. But there was nothing there. I stared at my trembling hands and my eyes were drawn to the left little finger.

What had she done? I knew in my heart that, whatever it was, it hadn't been an accident. She had cut it off herself. Had she been as unfamiliar with pain as she was with fear? Was it some twisted experiment to see if she could feel? Or was it something even more sinister?

Suddenly I remembered the story she'd told me about the old man. It hadn't really sunk in at the time. An allergic reaction, Mitzie had said. Now it occurred to me to wonder what kind of allergic reaction. To what exactly? And why had Mitzie seemed so smug about it?

My mind strayed back to the night she made us blood-sisters. My *sacrifice.* "Now you're a part of me," she'd said.

My skin crawled and again I brushed away imaginary wasps, recalling the unnatural shine in her eyes after the attack.

I've never seen anyone look so scared.

I didn't want to go back there but I knew I would never rest until I faced the truth. The moon hung high and bright overhead as I made my way down the street and across to her side of town. The funhouse loomed in silhouette, its splintered boards like claws raking at the night sky.

The door was open and I stepped inside, half expecting Mitzie to jump out at me. But there was no need for that now. I had no fear left to give her.

When I heard the buzzing again I didn't scream. I'd known it would be there. The noise surrounded me like mist and I closed my eyes, holding very still.

"Hello, Mitzie," I said.

The buzzing intensified for a moment, then subsided to a murmur.

Her voice was soft when it came. "Open your eyes."

I did. Moonlight streamed through the empty windows, illuminating the funhouse. There were no wasps. Only Mitzie.

For a moment she looked like a normal little girl again. And maybe she'd truly been that once. But now that little girl was gone and in her place was something else.

"Tell me what you did," I said.

She gazed at me, her eyes glinting in the pale light like an animal's. "You were always so fearful, so easy to scare," she began. "But that day in the tree... I'd never seen anything like that before. All I could think was that I wanted it."

"Wanted what?"

"Their power. You were terrified. You thought you were going to die. You even thought of jumping out of the tree. You knew it would kill you but you thought it anyway. I saw it all in your mind."

The pieces were coming together at last.

"The old man," I said.

She nodded. "He was scared too. But that was just a jarful released into his house. It was nothing like what happened to you. He got off easy."

All around me I could hear the rustling of wings, the scratching of tiny legs crawling over the rotting walls of the shack. Mitzie didn't seem to hear it. I looked down at the floor. The yellow smear was still there, luminous in the moonlight.

She smiled and held up her hand for me to see. The skin over the stump was stretched thin and tight, glistening with an unnatural sheen. "My sacrifice," she said. "Your gift. For the power."

She was insane. That much was clear. But there was far more at work here than just one little girl's madness.

"It doesn't work like that, Mitzie."

She shook her head and frowned. "What do you mean?"

My skin tingled with the memory of tiny legs clambering over it all night, climbing in and out of me. I couldn't answer her. I didn't know how to tell her she'd got it terribly wrong.

Mitzie looked disappointed, as though I'd failed to grasp some simple concept. "Don't you see?" She showed me the mangled finger stump again. "I released you."

I instinctively curled my own fingers, remembering the pain when she had pricked me with the needle, the way she had licked away my blood. The promise I had made was now just a smudge on the floor at my feet. Mitzie had made a different promise, to something else entirely.

"Don't *you* see? You killed one of them. Tortured it."

"It was an offering. We suffered together."

She still didn't realise what she'd done. All that fear. She'd tended it like flowers in a garden. It was here with us now, massing in the forest and in the rotting boards of the funhouse. My own fear was part of it, had helped create it. Mitzie had always believed she was the one in control, but she was wrong.

The air around her began to shimmer and the room grew suddenly cold. As I watched, her skin took on a sickly glow. Her eyes widened and I saw her afraid for the very first time. The *only* time. She opened her mouth to scream but the sound died in her throat. Shadows passed over her body in long, wavering stripes. Then the skin itself began to ripple and contort, as though thousands of living things were inside it, struggling to hatch.

And then they did hatch. The flesh at her throat split first, spilling forth a crawling swarm of wasps. They scuttled over one another in a buzzing frenzy, their wings vibrating, their antennae quivering. I saw their tiny jaws working furiously, devouring the shell from which they had emerged, leaving no trace of it behind.

Then, in a burst of wild humming, they formed into a cloud, billowing around me. My heart was pounding but there was nothing for me to fear any more. They moved with eerie precision and I saw how beautiful they could be. I reached a hand up into their swirling masses and they flowed over me like rain.

Thana Niveau is a horror and science fiction writer. Originally from the States, she now lives in the UK, in a Victorian seaside town between Bristol and Wales. She has twice been nominated for the British Fantasy award—once for her debut short story collection, *From Hell to Eternity*, and once for her story "Death Walks

En Pointe".

She has been writing all her life, but only began to publish after winning first place in a Jack the Ripper short story competition in 2010. Many others stories followed, in such diverse publications as *Interzone, Steampunk Cthulhu, Zombie Apocalypse: Endgame, Terror Tales of Wales,* and several volumes of *The Black Book of Horror* series. Her work has been reprinted in *The Mammoth Book of Best New Horror,* as well as *Best British Horror.* Her Lovecraftian novella *Not to Touch the Earth* is due out in early 2015.

Discover more at www.thananiveau.com.

Standing Behind the Curtains
A CONVERSATION WITH T.E.D. KLEIN

by Barry Lee Dejasu

In the early 1980's, horror fiction had reached a wider audience than ever before. Authors such as Peter Straub, Clive Barker, Ramsey Campbell, and of course Stephen King raised the standards of writing quality, deftly scaling the summits of popularity and bringing the genre to a new level of literary appreciation. Among their ranks was a writer named T.E.D. Klein, who would ultimately become one of the most important voices in modern horror fiction.

Theodore Donald Klein (the "E" stands for "Eibon," a literary reference to Clark Ashton Smith's Hyperborean sorcerer) was born and raised in New York. A graduate of Brown University, Klein would later study at Columbia, which led to a stint in the late 1970's at Paramount as a script reader. In 1981, he became the founding editor of the highly acclaimed *Rod Serling's Twilight Zone Magazine*, publishing works by authors such as Stephen King, Peter Straub, and Harlan Ellison before parting ways in 1985.

In 1984, Klein published his first, and so far only, novel, *The Ceremonies*. An expansion of an earlier novella named "Events at Poroth Farm" (itself inspired by "The White People," a classic short story by Welsh dark fantasy author Arthur Machen), *The Ceremonies* was an excursion into cosmic horror set against the backdrop of contemporary American culture. The novel enjoyed a brief ride on the *New York Times* Bestseller List, and although it's now long out of print, it is considered a classic.

The following year, Klein released a collection of four novellas, titled *Dark Gods*. Although three of its novellas were previously published elsewhere (namely Kirby McCauley's legendary 1980 anthology *Dark Forces*), one of them, "Nadelman's God," was original to the collection, and would subsequently go on to win the 1986 World Fantasy Award for Best Novella. And just like *The Ceremonies*, *Dark Gods* is unfortunately very much out of print.

As the years went by, Klein would only go on to publish less than a dozen short stories, most of which (along with "Events At Poroth Farm") were collected in a 2006 limited-edition book from Subterranean Press, *Reassuring Tales*. As with his previous works, this has unfortunately become an out-of-print rarity, and due to its limited print run (only 600 signed and numbered copies exist), it's even harder to find than the others, often being listed for over $100 online.

Klein may have estranged himself from the genre that he helped shape, but even after nearly three decades, his influence has never been forgotten. To date, authors such as Thomas Ligotti, John Langan, Laird Barron, Paul Tremblay, and Simon Strantzas look fondly upon his work as a direct influence upon their own.

In a rare and exclusive gesture, Mr. Klein broke his silence to generously discuss his life, writings, and career.

~

BLD. While you were growing up, what did you like to read? Who were some authors that you just couldn't get enough of, and not necessarily in horror?

TK. I loved a series of maritime adventure books by Howard Pease (or rather, by one of the authors with that name; there appear to have been two), who wrote about tramp steamers plying the South Seas. As a boy, I used to clip out the daily shipping news from the back of the *Times*—those listings still seem pretty romantic to me—and I imagined, crazily enough, that I would someday ship out on a rusted freighter and visit all sorts of exotic ports of call. Actually, I'm a lousy traveler and have always been afraid of the water.

My favorite childhood book had also been my father's favorite: Booth Tarkington's *Penrod* trilogy, in a thick black omnibus volume with my father's name stamped all over it. It's basically an early-twentieth-century *Tom Sawyer,* albeit a little more domesticated, and the writing's extremely droll. I read the book again and again and still remember many lines from it—like the description of a caterpillar motionless on a twig, looking as if it were "lost in reverie." Two friends from the neighborhood and I were even inspired to form a secret club we called the P.S. of A.P.B. (which stood for "the Penrod and Sam of All Penrod Books").

BLD. Around what age did you become interested in writing? What were some of your earliest writings about?

TK. At a point (probably in junior high), when I had read most of the celebrated Robert Heinlein juveniles and was moving on to the stuff for older readers, I remember getting involved in a writing competition with a brainy friend over who could complete a book first. He was going to write a history of the world (I said he was brainy), and I was going to write a science fiction novel. Neither one of us got very far, but I remember a few things my manuscript contained that, at the time, struck me as extremely neat but may well have been cribbed from things I'd read. I had my hero, a Heinleinesque space cadet, finish his training in a graduation ceremony that ended, symbolically, with each new graduate being shoved off the rostrum into a pit of mud. There was a space-travel scene (also Heinlein-inspired, I'm sure) in which a sleek rocket ship brought travelers up to some sort of giant, drab, ungainly interstellar transport chamber, floating somewhere beyond the moon, inside of which they stood around impatiently like a crowd of commuters in the main hall of Grand Central Station, smoking cigarettes and chatting; and when they filed out a few minutes later, they were at the other end of the galaxy. And there was a time traveler who miscalculated and somehow materialized where a brick wall had once been standing (or would someday be standing), "and before he could be rescued," I wrote, "his heart had turned to cement."

BLD. What about dark fiction appealed to you so much, to read it and to write it?

TK. Well, I think it just makes the world more interesting; [I gather] you mean what's usually described as "supernatural horror." A world with room in it for the supernatural would be both darker and potentially lighter than the one I believe we're actually living in; it would be a world richer in meaning, scarier and yet more charming. On the other hand, if there were even an ounce of religion among the things I happen to believe in (and there isn't), supernatural fiction would probably hold little appeal for me. I'd have no emotional need for it.

As for writing it, I suppose initially there's the normal desire to imitate the authors who've given one pleasure, followed later by the desire to modify, critique, and even poke fun at those same formative figures. (I guess you'd file that under "anxiety of influence.") Plus (and I'm sure this has been said a million times) for anyone who's ever been frightened, as I have, by a scary story or a horror film, there's a certain gratification in creating something of the same sort yourself, where it's you that's standing behind the curtains, controlling the action. It's akin to the reassurance a child may feel when he sees a behind-the-scenes photo of the guy in the rubber monster suit, or learns the secret of how special effects are produced, or gets the autograph, at a horror convention, of some actor who once scared him in the movies.

BLD. It's pretty obvious (from the themes and subject matter of your works) that you were a fan of Lovecraft and Machen. When did you get into them?

TK. I first encountered those writers in the most commonplace, boring old way— by coming across their work at my local library (in that celebrated Modern Library Giant, most likely). Later, at college in Providence, I found myself strolling daily through Lovecraft's beloved old neighborhood, buying Arkham House books at a shop he himself had frequented, and, during my senior year, living next door to a house that figures in "The Call of Cthulhu."

So for a while, I really became quite consumed with HPL—with his life as well as his fiction. Plus I've always had a tremendous fondness for New England, and Lovecraft is surely a key part of that; he's made it (the entire region, crazy as this may sound) a somewhat magical place.

BLD. If you don't mind my asking, which house had you lived in? (I myself am a Providence resident, and was born only a couple of blocks away from Lovecraft's own birthplace.)

TK: It's great that you were born so near HPL's birthplace. That's certainly one of the charms of Providence—feeling that his presence is so close. The house I lived in was the Deacon Edward Taylor House, 9 Thomas Street. I loved that building and felt grateful to be living in it. I remember the third floor, where I lived, had wide plank floorboards (creaking slightly, I think) and fireplaces in all four rooms.

BLD. Were any of your stories, or even *The Ceremonies*, ever optioned for film?

TED. Some blessed person did option *The Ceremonies* a few years ago, but obviously nothing has come of it. And a filmmaker in England has an option on "Children of the Kingdom." I wish him luck.

BLD. How does it feel to know how much your work has been a direct influence upon many established and renowned authors, such as Thomas Ligotti and Laird Barron?

TK: I'm actually astonished to hear that anyone's ever said such a thing; it's news to me. I'm pleased, I guess, but it's awfully hard to imagine anyone being influenced by anything of mine, especially considering how little I've managed to turn out.

BLD. Your work is *very* highly regarded. In fact, you have an entire stretch of a chapter in S.T. Joshi's *The Modern Weird Tale: A Critique of Horror Fiction*, right alongside Shirley Jackson, William Peter Blatty, Stephen King, Clive Barker, Ramsey Campbell, and Robert Bloch.

TK. That sort of thing is always a bit shocking to hear, but very nice, obviously.

BLD. Back in the '80's, you'd announced work on a new novel. Whatever became of that? Did you just never finish it, or is it pending heavy edits and in some sort of hiatus?

TK. Yes, it was going to be called *Nighttown*; it still may be! I got around halfway through, by which time I began to worry that it was getting out of hand; I mean, getting too long and complicated. (I had originally intended it to be a lively, fast-moving read, on the order of *The 39 Steps*, but clearly that sort of thing isn't a natural fit.) And then, unfortunately, I got distracted, which is always a problem. I find writing quite difficult, and I'm good at finding ways to avoid it.

BLD. So what did you end up doing instead? What have you been up to since?

TK. Thanks for asking. Life is definitely full of distractions, if you're looking for them. At one point, in the early '90s, when I should have been hard at work on the new book, I happily spent my time editing a true-crime magazine called *CrimeBeat*, which made a bit of a splash on newsstands but alas ran out of money after fourteen issues; though while it lasted it was great fun and something I'd always wanted to do. (I should add that although it was based on my own proposal, the initial capital was raised by my old mentor from *Twilight Zone*, Eric Protter, who died this past year; as did, more recently, my agent, Kirby McCauley; as did, even more recently, Alice Turner of *Playboy*. All three were friends I was very close to, for decades, and to whom I owe a lot.)

During that same period (this time thanks to Kirby), I also had the chance to write a screenplay for the Italian director Dario Argento, adapted from a treatment of his. The movie itself (*Trauma*, 1983) turned out to be unwatchable; I, at least, have never managed to sit through it. (You know how Machen said something like "I dreamed in fire, but I worked in clay?" He might have been talking about that woeful little film.) Still, it was exciting to work on a script, and actually explore locations, with a colorful, amusing, albeit exasperating character like Argento.

Subsequently I did some teaching at John Jay College, part of the city university system. I enjoyed it. I once spent a year teaching high school English in Dexter, Maine—one of the best years of my life.

For the past decade, I've been working for *GQ*; my official title is senior copy editor. The senior part is appropriate, as I'm probably the oldest guy on the staff. Basically I spend my day inserting and deleting commas; I really know my commas. When I first got the job, my friend Margie said, "What? You're the most un-*GQ* person I've ever known." I still take that as a compliment. The company, Condé Nast, has just vacated its offices in the heart of Times Square and is now ensconced, for better or worse, in the new World Trade Center downtown. I can't say I'm warming to the place, and I expect to retire soon.

BLD. Would you ever consider returning to writing fiction again?

TK. Definitely, although I have to admit I'm somewhat less interested in horror fiction, and fiction in general, than I used to be; it's probably a consequence of age. I find I prefer to read big fat history books these days, and a smattering of popular science—trying to make up for too many years of ignorance.

BLD. Would you like to say anything to all the authors, artists, etc., who have been inspired by you over the years?

TK. I'm truly grateful, but now please try some good nonfiction!

BLD. Ted, this was a real honor. Thank you so much for your time!

TK. Thank you.

THE TALL MAN

by Eric J. Guignard

According to Guinness World Records, the tallest man in history was Robert Wadlow, who died in 1940 after reaching a height of eight feet, eleven inches. But I know someone taller, someone the record keepers won't acknowledge. It's not for oversight that Guinness fails to certify him... the Tall Man comes only for me.

He rises each midnight, a blot of shadow emerging from behind the cracks of a bedroom closet filled with nighttime terrors. The blot, at first indistinct, unfolds itself like unpacking a tightly pressed shirt. Accordion legs stretch up and origami arms extend, 'til a man is crushed beneath my ceiling, bent in half, his head pushed down above my clenched eyes, swallowing my exhalations.

He grows taller as I age, each of my breaths his nutrition. The Tall Man has yet to cause harm, though my fright grows larger with the years, as does he, until I tremble at each falling sun, knowing darkness is near, fearing his final satiation.

And that's another record the statisticians at Guinness won't acknowledge: For seventy-five years of continuous nights, I'm still tormented by the same bogeyman of my youth, once an insubstantial wisp, now a giant of a man.

Eric J. Guignard writes dark and speculative fiction from the outskirts of Los Angeles, and his works may be found in the disreputable publications reserved for back alley bazaars. As an editor, Eric has published the anthologies *Dark Tales of Lost Civilizations* and *After Death...*, the latter of which won the 2013 Bram Stoker Award®. Read his novella, *Baggage of Eternal Night* (a finalist for the 2014 International Thriller Writers Award), and watch for forthcoming books, including *Chestnut 'Bo* (TBP 2016).

Visit Eric at: www.ericjguignard.com, his blog: ericjguignard.blogspot.com, or Twitter: @ericjguignard.

WINTER FEVER

by Samuel Marzioli

Nick scooped another shovelful of snow from the walkway. The quiet and emptiness of his property—miles of grass and sedge buried by the previous day's flurry—made it a solemn act. Like a gravedigger, he felt obliged to shut his mouth and keep his head down until the task was finished.

He wiped sweat off his forehead, all too aware of the coming night. Already the sun had dipped below the line of his rooftop, causing the shadow of his house to warp and stretch and follow close behind him. There was something about it that made him uneasy. Not that he'd ever been fond of any dark space, but this one felt different, almost attentive. He kept imagining the shadow of the chimney stack as a black hand reaching for his heels, and no amount of backward glances settled his suspicion.

He paused and turned toward the house, to ground himself in the sight of it and calm his nerves. He wiped the sweat from his forehead again, but this time he felt heat burgeoning beneath his skin. The realization made him dizzy, almost nauseous.

Just need to sleep it off, he thought.

Tossing the shovel beneath the eaves, he dragged himself inside. Like every evening, before crawling into bed, he turned on the bedside lamp.

For the next few hours, his condition worsened. He struggled against the pain, forcing his body into awkward positions in a vain attempt to take the edge off. At times he managed to fall asleep. But the fever ruined any hope of true rest, tainting his dreams with maddening repetition—every one of them nightmares of unseen things whispering from the depths of endless, dark places.

Before he fell asleep for good, he remembered his mother's favorite warning, used whenever he misbehaved. She never bothered with lies about the Boogie Man or Santa Claus to keep him in line. Instead, she would just say, "Keep it up and the darkness will get you." Short. Effective. Unforgettable to a boy new to fear and steeped in imagination.

Despite the fire in his brain, he couldn't stop himself from shivering.

~

Nick burned too hot to think straight. Sweat soaked his pillow and sheets, filling the air with a cloying sweet-sick odor. Through the blinds, storm clouds huddled close, blocking out the sunlight and spilling a sheet of virgin snow into a false dusk.

"Wake up, Daddy!"

He recognized the voice, but it took a moment for the name to break through his fevered confusion.

"Sarah?" he said. The word felt strange. How many weeks, or months, had it been since he'd seen her last? Try as he might, the memory remained elusive and the pain of thinking soon forced him to relent. "Did your mother let you in? Is she here too?"

She leaned through the doorway, black hair done up in pigtails, cheeks pinched-red globes. The rest of her features remained obscured and blended into the insufficient light.

"No. The door was locked, but I found another way in," she said.

"I'm feeling pretty sick right now. Can you play in your room for a while?"

"But I'm hungry. It's time to eat."

He blinked once, rubbing his forehead with the meat of his palm.

"Sarah, I—"

He meant to say I can't, but the next thing he knew he was standing in the kitchen. The stovetop burner glowed red beneath a skillet lined with sizzling bacon and sausage. A single egg crowned the center. A click to his left alerted him that the rice cooker had finished. All the while, Sarah sat at the dining table with her fingers laced upon her lap. Smiling.

When he placed a heaping portion of the food in front of her, she gave it a perfunctory look. She poked at the egg with a fork—causing the yolk to pop and ooze—and then dropped it to her plate with a hollow clatter.

"Happy birthday?" she said.

"It's not my birthday."

"I meant happy birthday to me!"

He gave her a calm look, steadying himself against the tabletop, trying to hide the scalding guilt her words had made him feel.

"Maybe we can celebrate later when I'm feeling better," he said.

She shrugged, stood and skipped off down the hallway toward her room. He, in turn, stumbled to his bedroom and slipped back into bed.

~

Silence spread throughout the house, save for the rasp of heavy snow sliding off the rooftop. With the blinds closed, darkness smothered Nick's bedroom, thick as smoke and full of presence. He lay in bed, pretending to ignore it. Trying to convince himself he didn't feel it watching like before.

It embarrassed him to admit the sensation terrified him. It reminded him of when he was a boy. All those long and sleepless nights where shadows brimmed between his bedroom walls and choking on a pillow was the only thing that muffled the sound of his crying. Screaming did no good; his mother never came. With nowhere to run and no one to turn to, his hope had been to keep still and quiet until the morning banished every trace of night. In that way, some things never changed.

A scuffle on the carpet came from somewhere in the room. Nick groped for the bedside lamp, knocking it to the floor in the process. His heartbeat strained against his weakness, but even its meaty thumps failed to match the fear that gripped him. When he heard the sound again, closer to his side, he grabbed his pillow and swung it back and forth with all his breathless might.

"Daddy?"

He almost fell out of bed, but caught himself in time to collapse back to the mattress.

"I'm bored. Can we play in the dark?" said Sarah.

Her voice roamed about the room, from one end to another. Sometimes closer, sometimes farther away. And had he heard her question right, or was his mind playing tricks on him?

"What did you say?"

"I said can we go to the park?"

He only realized how tense he'd become when her answer eased him into a calmer state, and his body seemed to melt into the mattress.

"No, honey. It's much too far away. Besides, with the storm, leaving the house would be dangerous."

"Awww," she said.

He heard the bedroom door open and shut. Before he fell asleep again he righted the lamp and turned it on. He also opened the blinds, trying not to think too hard about who had even closed them.

~

Nick hunkered in the rear corner of the hallway closet, behind a tall stack of boxes. His mother sauntered through the house, searching for him.

"I can't believe you broke my mirror," she said. "Come out here, God damn it!" He imagined the wooden rod gripped between her plump, red fingers, its hum splitting the air with each practice swing she took. His back ached in anticipation and he covered his face behind crossed arms.

"If I don't find you, the darkness will. It feeds on the fear of wicked little children. It craves it. And when it's had its fill, it'll feed on you next."

At once, Nick recognized the mistake of his hiding place. Before, the dark around him lay vacant and inert. Now it stirred, as if it had become a living thing, caressing him with a feather touch that made his skin flare with goose bumps.

He opened his eyes and began to flail his arms. A deep moan escaped his throat. But when he recognized his own living room around him, he slumped into the couch beneath his body. He didn't know how he got there, but was glad the TV was on because it felt like the dark had closed in on him while he slept.

As if it had expanded its borders everywhere beyond the wide blue stream of the TV's light.

"Daddy," Sarah said, from somewhere in the hall. Her doorway, he guessed, because he couldn't see for sure. "Can I watch a show?"

"If you keep the volume low."

For a moment there was quiet. Then he heard the patter of footsteps closing in behind him.

"Can you turn the light on, please?" he said.

"Why?"

"I don't like the dark."

"What's wrong with the dark?"

"I dunno. Maybe it's because it gives the monsters a place to hide."

"Silly Daddy." She giggled. "If there were monsters, the light would only make them nervous."

He smiled. His baby girl had always been clever. More clever than him at that age, maybe even more clever than him now.

~

They played *Candyland* on the carpet of his daughter's room, the floor lamp veiled by a black t-shirt to protect his sensitive eyes. He was glad she brought the game because he didn't have anything else she could use to occupy her time. Just grown-up books, dusty bookcases and old furniture that filled up a lot of space.

The more he thought about it, the more he realized how much he'd missed her. Fever or not, he reveled in the comfort of her company, and he wondered why he hadn't thought to ask her over sooner. Not since—

"My turn," she said. She grabbed a card, crinkling a corner. "Ice cream cone!" She squealed and licked her lips. "Can I have some ice cream, Daddy?"

"Sorry, I don't have any."

"Then how about a snow cone?"

The shadow of her finger pointed toward the window, to the thick white layer of snow covering the glass.

"Just make sure you don't eat... the yellow stuff..."

His voice slid away, and with it went his surroundings. When he became aware again, he found himself slumped upon the toilet, pants bunched around his ankles. He felt wet below, somewhere between those pallid thighs that didn't quite feel a part of him, so he knew he had gone. But when?

He dropped a hand against the toilet roll. Only the cardboard tube remained. Collecting all his strength, he yelled, "Sarah, I need some toilet paper."

No response.

"Sarah?"

Maybe it was later than he imagined and she'd already gone to sleep. But somehow he knew she had heard him. Somehow, he could feel her behind the bathroom door, listening in the darkness of the hallway. A broad smile creasing her rosy cheeks.

~

The blinds allowed in a feeble glow, exposing the barest hint of shapes against the wall opposite the window. Just outside of its range, standing by the foot of his bed, he could see the outline of a figure. A tall thing, skinny as a pole, with its palms held flat against its belly.

Nick drew the covers up to his chin, twisting and pulling on its edges as if to rip the cloth in half. "Who's there? Who are you?" he said.

It took a few careful, short steps. A few more and then the light revealed it clearer, shrinking it down and widening it, until it had the shape of Sarah. She held out something rectangular, wrapped in a white sheet of paper.

"Open it," she said.

"Oh Sarah, you shouldn't have. I should be the one giving you a gift."

"You gave me life." She grinned, and what little of her face he could see burst with over-eagerness.

It reminded him of the broken toys and unwanted knickknacks she used to wrap and give away as gifts. Nick usually found himself staring down at a legless horse, or the head of a ceramic kitten, or some necklace missing all its plastic jewels. Whatever was inside this time, she must have brought with her. He tore a jagged line across the top and held it upside down. Photographs slipped into his hand, a stack thick as a finger.

"Do you like them?" she said.

He squinted at the topmost photo, could see various shades of colors, but nothing clear. Nothing concrete.

"What are they?"

"It's us. Our day together. Daddy-daughter pictures."

Nick smiled. "I love them. Thanks, sweetie. Tomorrow, we'll look at them together."

~

Nick opened his eyes. The clock perched above the doorframe announced the hour: 8 AM. For the first time since he had fallen ill, the room opened up to him, exposing walls and corners, the clarity of its many lines and colors. He sat up in bed, soaking up the pleasure of being well. Savoring the feel and brilliance of the daylight pouring through the open blinds.

Like every morning, before crawling out of bed, he turned off the bedside lamp. He went to the window next. Snow fell, thick and unrelenting, riled by a heavy wind that sent it whipping in all directions. He could see nothing past the perimeter of his backyard fence some fifty feet away, already buried to its upper rails. All that time shoveling the walkway had meant nothing; the storm had likely buried his car by now.

He was about to head to the bathroom when memories of his troubled dreams returned. Especially of the little girl who'd starred in every one, the details of their lives together filled by that same omniscient source that informed all dreams. He couldn't recall her name, but he remembered that she'd been his daughter, and how he'd never quite seen her face because it was always wrapped in shadows. He also remembered her gift from the last time they were together. He threw a glance to where his dream-self left it, to settle his idle curiosity.

Upon the table edge, closest to the bed, a sheet of crumpled printer paper lay curled around a pile of photographs. Confusion rattled in the empty space between his thoughts. It took some coaxing before he gathered enough nerve to examine them more closely.

In the first, he saw himself standing on the walkway, holding a shovel and staring at the house. In the next, he lay in bed, an arm draped across his face. Then, he was standing in front of the stove, eyes shut, arms limp and dangling by his side. Another in bed. One of him asleep on the couch. One in the empty office, sprawled across the carpet. One passed out upon the toilet. Another in bed. And another, and another, and another.

He flung the photos to the ground and shoved a fist into his mouth. His legs scissored against the urine threatening to explode from his bladder. There came a sharp knock on the door.

"Did you like my photos, Daddy?" the soft, almost singsong voice behind it said. Blackness rippled beneath the door gap.

"Sarah," he said, remembering her name at last.

"Yes, Daddy?"

"You're not my daughter, God damn it. I don't even know you."

Her giggles lingered, overlapping her response. "I may not be your flesh and blood, but you made me just the same. Fear was my mommy. That fear was your intimate companion. Through the years it gave me substance, gave me shape and life. And that's what makes you Daddy."

The center of the door began to bulge. Tendrils of shadow pushed through the cracks of its edges, lapping at the air within his bedroom like thirsty tongues.

Nick spun around to face the window. Ten miles separated him from his closest neighbor and twice that to the nearest town—assuming he could find them without following the road. He took a stuttered breath as he threw the blinds aside. Then he jerked the window open and stared into the endless white and searing cold that buffeted his face.

The door gave out a sickening crack and toppled to the floor. Without a backward glance, he leaped through the open window, landing barefoot on a cushion of snow. The last thing he heard before the storm swallowed him whole was the sound of Sarah's voice, singing, "Happy birthday to me."

Samuel Marzioli was born and raised, and that's all you need to know about that. His work has appeared or is forthcoming in numerous publications, including *Apex Magazine, Intergalactic Medicine Show, Penumbra eMag,* and *A Darke Phantastique* (2014). You can find more information about his current projects from his website, marzioli.blogspot.com.

BLOODSTAIΠS & BLUE SUEDE SHOES

by John Boden and Barry Lee Dejasu

PART VIII: THE NINETIES AND THE NEW MILLENIUM

By the time the nineties were in full swing, there was a much broader saturation in rock radio by a much wider variety of musical styles. The heavy hitters from the "grunge explosion" were still around and strangling folks with their flannel flags; Soundgarden was getting less dark and broody and going for a radio-friendly hard rock sound, and many of their peers followed suit, with bands like Nine Inch Nails and Ministry still throwing out bricks of electronic angst and self-loathing. Yet like with many styles of music, the large shift in the commercial consensus of mainstream contemporary tastes led to the rise of a new, dark hope in the underground scene.

DON'T BOTHER TO RESIST, OR I'LL BEAT YOU

In late 1994, Florida's Marilyn Manson delivered a debut entitled *Portrait of An American Family* that was so ridiculously over-the-top and dark that even the most jaded of music fans sat up and took note. Looking like the drugged out love children of Raggedy Ann and Andy, if said incestuous offspring were dressed up like the New York Dolls, the band was sleazy, glammy, and evil as fuck. Songs about addiction, monsters, bugs, incest and many other sordid topics didn't win them any fans among parents, but the kids couldn't shell out their lunch money quick enough. The video for their hit single "Dope Hat" was a nightmarish retooling of the infamous "boat ride" sequence from the film *Charlie & The Chocolate Factory*. Manson would prove more than a fly-by-night creature, as he's still releasing danceable dark music over twenty years later. It is interesting to note that at this time, even Christian music was attempting to cash in on the young people's appetite for destruction by releasing work by decidedly dark bands like Rackets & Drapes, Saviour Machine, and Wedding Party.

HOW DEEP CAN I GO IN THE GROUND THAT I LAY?

That same year and onward saw bands like Korn, Deftones, and Deadsy rise from the metal pools and continue to forge a new sound. Korn unleashed their raw and unpolished deep end stomp while Deftones went for a more melodic but no less brutal path. An underground favorite was Deadsy, fronted by Elijah Blue Allman (son of Cher and Gregg Allman), who played a deeply eighties sound but with heavier riffs and a low-end Goth mood (unfortunately, their self-titled debut never saw a release until it was re-recorded almost ten years later through Korn's record label). In the wake of these and other first-wave alternative metal bands, a slew of other groove-based bands such as Orgy, Mudvayne, and Static-X came crawling out of the woodwork, headlining the Ozzfest scene while simultaneously carving out a whole new subgenre later known as "nu-metal."

While rock radio and TV began clamoring for any and every nu-metal band they could find, metal was still alive and well. In South America and other countries, melodic metal and eighties-styled metal thrived. In the United States, extreme metal and grindcore was terrorizing teens that were thirsty for more; death metal bands like Cannibal Corpse, Morbid Angel, Cryptopsy, and Broken Hope were delivering the gore-soaked goods.

GLISTENING AND NEW, THE SUNSET'S COMING

From the swamps of Louisiana came the sludge metal band Acid Bath. Audiences didn't know what was hitting them when they saw that the cover for their 1994 full-length debut, *When the Kite String Pops*, featured the artwork of serial-killing enthusiast John Wayne Gacy. Acid Bath delivered horrifying songs about nightmares and screamingly surreal images, the titles of which speak for themselves: "Cassie Eats Cockroaches," "Finger Paintings of the Insane," and "The Bones of Baby Dolls." They followed with the album *Paegan Terrorism Tactics*, which featured a lovely Easter painting by Dr. Jack Kevorkian as cover art. The band broke up soon after the tragic death of their bassist Audie Pitre, who was killed along with his parents when they were hit head-on by a drunk driver in 1997, but his musical legacy lives on.

Elsewhere in the world, many bands were taking extreme metal into experimental territories, likely taking something of a cue from the birth of alternative music in the US. England's autopsy- and dictionary-influenced Carcass began to focus on dishing out brilliant metal harmonies and darkly philosophical songs, with their 1994 album *Heartwork* being a watershed for the birth of melodic death metal. Not long after, a multitude of bands in Sweden such as Dark Tranquillity, In Flames, and Soilwork continued this movement of progressive and/or melodic metal.

PAGAN FEARS—THE PAST IS ALIVE!

Deep inside the dark forests of Norway, many angry young musicians began to churn out buzzsaw riffs, dizzyingly fast rhythms, and screeching, tortured vocals, spinning lyrics about everything from ancient Norse mythology, the occult, Satanism, and of course death. It was a sound that could cause even the most callously "extreme" metalhead's ears bleed—a sound that triumphantly took up the moniker of black metal. Bands such as Bathory and Venom had already established some of the basic themes and tones of the black metal scene back in the mid-to-late eighties, but when the early nineties hit, the likes of Mayhem, Darkthrone, Emperor, and Burzum soon burned their way into the headlines—sometimes literally. Hate crimes, arson, suicide and murder went hand-in-hand with the bloody rise of the Norwegian black metal scene, defining what may be the ugliest example of the darkness that music can bring out of people.

Doom, gloom and other unpleasant subject matters weren't limited to the heavier side of music in the nineties. Cult favorite Nick Cave and his Bad Seeds released several albums brimming with a thread of unease—a pinnacle of which could be the Grammy-nominated *Murder Ballads* album, which as the title informs is an album of songs about murder and mayhem.

The dark music of the nineties has very easily survived the shift into the new millennium. Horror, death, doom, and despair are alive and well in the metal scene, with bands such as The Horrors, Lordi, and Crobot churning out the dark stuff. Musicians such as Dax Riggs (ex-Acid Bath frontman) are still singing about dark demons and swirling madness as the world burns. Even mellower acts such as Simone Felice and Josh Ritter thrive in darkness; Felice's song "New York Times" is one of the most sinisterly haunting songs ever, and Ritter's lovely ballad about a mummy, "The Curse," must be heard to fully bask in its brilliance.

Many an act refuses to shy away from such subject matter as death and monsters, demons and bloodshed; that stuff is as much the fiber of society as anything else, and frankly, a lot less scary than what clogs our news feeds on a daily basis. As with every personal taste, there are those who like their music fun, hopeful, uplifting, and light...and then there are those of us that wear headphones in the dark, tapping our feet along to a very old rhythm in bloodstained, blue suede shoes.

John Boden lives in the shadow of Three Mile Island, where he bakes cakes and cookies for a living. Any remaining time is unevenly divided between his amazing wife and sons, working for Shock Totem, and his own writing. His unique fiction has appeared in *52 Stitches, Metazen, Weirdyear, Black Ink Horror #7, O Little Town of Deathlehem, Radical Dislocations, Splatterpunk 5,* and *Psychos: Serial Killers, Depraved Madmen, and the Criminally Insane,* edited by John Skipp. His not-for-children children's book, *Dominoes,* was published in 2013. He has work forthcoming in *Blight Digest, Once Upon an Apocalypse Vol. I, Despumation Magazine,* and *Halloween Forevermore.* He has stunning muttonchops and a heart of gold.

Barry Lee Dejasu is a regular contributor to the movie website Cinema Knife Fight, for which he writes a column, "Scoring Horror," featuring interviews with movie composers. In addition to *Shock Totem,* his fiction has appeared in Four

Horsemen's *Anthology: Year Three: Distant Dying Ember.* He lives and works in Providence, Rhode Island, with his partner, author Catherine Grant.

THE EAVESDROPPER

by Sarah L. Johnson

*D*on't let them see your face, the ones who dwell in the hollow. It's the water, you see. Lakes, pools, even a puddle will do. Any dark standing water big enough to hold a reflection. Like ghosts behind a mirror, they're drawn to the surface, to that thin membrane separating our world from theirs. They exist in emptiness. They are hungry. They are cold.

And more than anything, they want out.

I've heard the stories, the warnings, and the rules. It's important to listen. A good listener hears all manner of things.

Grass whispers under bare feet. Insects whine and chirp. A few houses down, one cat yowls at another and that is a sound I do not care for—the grinding winding anthem of bad ideas. I much prefer the curious flap of sheets forgotten on the line and the *shuck-shuck-shuck* of sprinklers.

The velvet hush of grass gives way to the scrape of gravel. Near the water's edge, even the darkness makes a sound. They say that in the hollow, that's the only sound there is.

Don't taunt them. A pebble kicked into the pond shatters the moon into countless ripples. A silver-white massacre.

Don't get too close. On hands and knees now, leaning over the water, just a bit. A face appears, distorted and disturbed. Does it see me?

Don't touch the water at night. A fingertip breaches the surface, and a cold meniscus hugs the knuckle. The salt and shiver of blood and bone, sliding deeper.

I've heard them speak of this also. *You'll know when they're near, because you'll tremble and sweat, wishing to be anywhere but where you are, and yet you'll crave the darkness of the hollow like you've craved nothing else in all your days.*

Come to think of it, everything I've heard them say about the hollow is true—everything except darkness being the only sound. How would they know?

The truth is that within that darkness we hear many things, but the thing we hear best, is you.

Well met, my friend. Now, if you please, just a little closer.

Let me out.

Sarah L. Johnson lives in Calgary where she runs marathons, blogs about Nabokov, and makes pie crust with vodka. Her short fiction has appeared in a number of journals and anthologies including *Crossed Genres*, *Room Magazine*, and the Bram Stoker nominated *Dark Visions 1*. Her first novel, *Infractus*, will be published by **Driven Press** in 2016. You can visit her at www.sarahljohnson.com.

THE LAST TREEHOUSE

by David G. Blake

Current location registered on the mainframe—fourth quadrant of the Separation; within sensor range of the Zion Nebula—an instant before the piloting station door hissed open. There was no need for Jack to turn to see who had entered. He smelled cinnamon apple spice, Avery's favorite lotion, and heard the asthmatic hitch in her breath, which she often had when upset. He also felt her antipathy clamp onto his back like a plutonium monkey with a death grip.

The ship juddered, adjusting its equilibrium. Avery held her footing and slammed the copilot seat into position. A nondescript band held her red hair in a severe ponytail. It forced her freckles to stand out like a cluster of distress beacons. Jack sought to look at her as a man should look at his wife but again failed to penetrate those hard green eyes, which reflected his own resentment a hundredfold.

"Where are we?"

"Near the Zion Nebula," he replied, charting coordinates that would ultimately steer them deeper into the scattered clouds of gas and dust ahead. "Fourth quadrant of the Separation."

"Don't you think it's time you let me in on our destination?"

"Mara wants trees and beaches and white sand. You want security. I just want to keep you both safe and happy."

"Cut the spiel, Jack. Only thing I want right now is to know where we're headed."

"Does it *really* matter? I'm taking us to a place where the Zetrians won't find us. Leave me to it."

She stood and moved toward the exit. "They won't stop looking just because we stop running."

"I don't expe—"

The door hissed shut. Jack popped the copilot seat up with his foot. He knew that Avery hated the *unsettling emptiness of space*—her words—while he found it serene and anything save empty, one of their numerous differences. If Vyndrae proved half as perfect as the logbook Jack had swiped described, Avery would find it impossible to stay angry. Even at him.

Estimated time of arrival blinked on the overhead: three hours and seven minutes. That *should* carry them deep enough to avoid immediate detection, the density of the nebula working as a natural buffer against long-range scans. It would also provide the time to isolate Vyndrae's precise location. But the possibility that the Zetrians were closer than expected left Jack feeling ill and more than a little paranoid. Three-plus hours might prove just long enough to rob him of any real chance of escape.

He increased engine power to maximum—ETA dropped by one hour and twenty-two minutes—and cringed as the stolen ship creaked and groaned in response. If he pressed deep enough, *fast enough*, no one would ever trace them. The ship simply needed to remain intact until they landed on Vyndrae.

~

Jack cycled the engine, the rough final leg of the journey lending a measure of rawness to its dying whir. They had made it to Vyndrae swiftly enough for him to feel confident that no one would locate them, but he still had the system run a diagnostic check to guarantee the ship was in shape to flee if needed. Recent events had taught him the wisdom of preparation. And making it here intact was no longer good enough...not for him and his.

While he waited, he calibrated the scanner, enabled its mobile functionality, and clipped it to his belt. A dark green light showed that the diagnostic check had not found any issues. He activated the security sphere around the ship and opened the outer hatch. It was time to explore their new home.

The sky-above had been breathtaking. Vyndrae, the planet that promised security and a new start—and beaches, trees, and white sand to spare—had unfolded from the interstellar dust and gas clouds like a flower opening to the sun. Blue oceans covered the bulk of her, as though she had wrapped the sky round her with a keen sense of modesty, but lush green gems ringed in ivory adorned her body and hinted at coming fulfillment.

Yet the sky-below held treasures of its own. A bolt of lightning the color of an Enceladus plume tore across the sky and bled pink particles in its wake. The air shuddered with the soft cry of thunder. Over the horizon, the sun loomed large and ominous. But the gathering of iridescent clouds of gas and dust in the mesosphere—near twins of those in the sky-above—allowed life on Vyndrae to flourish. Information the logbook made a point to address. Jack knew it well enough to quote from its tattered pages.

A creature similar to a mimic octopus, tentacles flattened outward like wings, jettisoned across the sky feeding off the pink particles. Maroon-tailed birds with sunlit blue wings circled above, noticeably avoiding the lively octopus. Below, so close to the water the waves wet their gray feathers, a flock of smaller birds hovered, taking turns diving below the surface to snatch fish in their long rapier-like beaks.

Avery and Mara stood hand-in-hand on the beach looking up with shared expressions of wonderment. A dank breeze, which tasted of brine and smelled of burnt ozone, rolled in off the sea and ruffled their matching red hair. They were as near the rim of the security sphere as they could safely get and had removed their shoes and buried their toes in the warm white sand.

"What do you think?"

Mara slid her hand into his. "It's perfect, Papa."

Even Avery agreed. "It is beautiful, Jack."

"I'm glad you both approve." He squeezed Mara's hand and pointed skyward. "See the creature chasing lightning?"

"Looks like an octopus."

"It sure does. The logbook I found had a drawing of a similar creature. The captain kept it as a pet."

"Think it's the same one?" The notion clearly roused her imagination.

"Could be. But if it *is*, it's over a century old." He pulled her close and tickled under her chin. "It might be its little girl!"

She giggled and twisted free—shoulders up and head to the side—and ran a few feet away before pointing inland toward the trees. "Check it out!"

Behind them stretched the forest, beginning a short distance from where he had landed the ship. The trees swayed, yellowish-orange leaves reflecting sunlight like fragments of pure amber. Their rustling leaves and creaking limbs made it sound as though they were greeting the three of them, welcoming them to Vyndrae. Further scrutiny revealed, nestled midst those same trees, what had stirred Mara's curiosity.

"Is it a treehouse, Papa?"

"Sure looks like it, sweetheart."

Avery stepped closer, sand shifting beneath her bare feet. "Was a *treehouse* in that book of yours?"

"Not that I read." He detached the scanner from his belt. "But it's possible the captain mentioned it on one of the damaged pages."

"Damaged? I hope you are just trying to be funny."

"It's an old logbook, Avery, and in poor condition."

"And you didn't find that worth mentioning?"

"Maybe it was, maybe it wasn't. But it's *definitely* not worth arguing about right now."

He turned away from her and used the scanner to decrease the density of the security sphere. The air crackled, and a blue field materialized around the ship. It thrummed with an intensity that drowned out the native sounds of Vyndrae, and amplified into a piercing whine once he neared the rim. If passed through at such a low setting it would only tickle and raise hackles. The less protection it offered the louder and more visible it became to compensate.

"Better have a look, Jack. If we aren't alone..."

~

A sharp incline bordered the trees. Odd little crabs—blue and yellow with two oversized white eyes atop stubby antennae—scuttled over the sand and under the rocks, surprised by Jack's approach. He ignored them best he could and focused on the jagged rocks and warped roots that jutted from the side of the outlet. A number of crabs scampered over his boots whenever he took a breather, but none remained in sight long.

Jack's boots sank in the soft moss of the forest floor, and the trees no longer appeared so welcoming. They felt akin to a savage tribe of giants singing and dancing to the war beat of the wind. The reality that he was an invader had never been clearer than it was standing under such strange beings who spoke even stranger tongues. If you failed to understand the trees and could not sense the rhythm of the wind, how much more of an outsider could you be?

He forced aside the sudden melancholy and moved closer, immediately noticing several other treehouses, though the one Mara spotted appeared to be the only one left standing. Trees had crushed the others in their wooden grasp and devoured them with their amber teeth. Only a smattering of crumbs remained, strewn amongst the treetops like sacrifices to the maroon-tailed birds that used the pieces to build nests high above the rocks and roots and scuttling crabs.

A staircase led upward, where a rope dangled off the side and twined into a pile near a bed of yellow and white mushrooms—or similar-looking gilled fungi. Near the lip of the roof extended a long stick, a dingy strip of cloth tied around it. Jack scaled to the top and surprised two orange lizards from railing to tree. They scurried down together and vanished beneath the scattered leaves. Once the sound of their escape died down, all remained quiet, even the trees.

Inside, caked with dust and grime, was a well-built table—he could already picture Mara having imaginary friends over for a tea party—and an equally fine chair. Faded markings dotted the walls, crude drawings or perhaps symbols of an alien sort. He rubbed a section with his right sleeve, dismayed to see white powder come clean along with the dust and grime. Somewhat like chalk. Used to scrawl the markings, most likely.

Turning attention to the stability of the treehouse, Jack stomped around a bit and knocked on the walls, listening closely. It felt solid and sounded the same. It would be the ideal setting to encourage Mara's imagination to flourish. Perhaps it would even alleviate some of the loneliness of being the only child around. She needed something...*they* needed something.

He used the rope to get down; it pleased him to find it capable of holding his weight with no sign of fraying. Once he reached the mossy forest floor—careful to avoid the cluster of fungi at his feet—he gave the rope a fierce tug. Though it held fast, he could not see allowing Mara to play inside the treehouse with the rope there tempting her. The whole area needed work to make it safe, a lot of work. The rope would be the first thing to go.

~

"I don't care for that treehouse," Avery said for the thousandth time. "You wasted a week fixing it up when you should've just finished it off." She motioned toward the shelter, which Jack had been working on for the past three days. "Looks like you could use the wood."

"Mara's enjoying herself, Avery. Let the blasted treehouse be. She deserves it."

"Don't talk to me about what Mara deserves...don't you *dare*. If you had listened back on Detra, we would not have such concerns, but you got greedy and refused to quit before things got out of control. She could have had a real life, Jack. *That* is what she deserves."

"I made mistakes—that's true—but I like it here and so does Mara. She's making the best of a bad situation. Why can't you?"

"You're impossible."

Before he could snap off an appropriate retort, Mara rushed into the clearing waving a doll in her hands, its torn white dress streaked with stains. "Look what I found!"

"Put that down, Mara, right this instant," Avery said. "It's filthy."

"What's the harm?" Jack asked, shooting Avery a pointed glare. "Let her be a kid for a change." He smiled at Mara. "Where'd you find it, sweetheart?"

"On the table in the treehouse. Isn't she just beautiful?"

He frowned, wondering how he had missed it while working. "Are you certain that's where you found it?"

She nodded, showing him a piece of chalk clenched in her fist. "I drew her on the wall first, because the treehouse told me to, and *then* I found her. I think this is magic chalk."

Avery snorted. "Stop telling fibs. You know better."

"I'm not!"

"It's okay, sweetheart. It doesn't matter where—"

"See!" Mara pointed skyward. "It told me to draw *that*, too."

Clouds as black as the deepest regions of space rolled across the sky, boiling forth from one focal point—a whirl of sunglow and sea weaved through with lightning. Below, a mist off the waves spread toward the shore, swallowing the flock of small birds that still hovered above the water; the maroon-tailed birds had already fled, as had the octopus.

"It looks..." He had no words.

Avery clutched at his arm. "We need to get to the ship. Fast." Even so close, she had to scream in order for him to hear her over the storm.

Jack grabbed Mara and made sure Avery kept hold of his other arm. They reached the hatch an instant before white-hot hail punched through the security sphere and sizzled into the sand. Raw electricity lit the dark, midday sky, sparks skipping along the hull. Jack amplified sphere density to full. The field dematerialized and hail began bouncing off the air around the ship, the sparks disappearing from the hull.

Mara clung to him. "I'm scared, Papa. I'm sorry I drew the storm. I wanted it to be a nice one, like when we watched the rain together back home. I just wanted to do that again."

The sentiment crushed him. "It isn't your fault, sweetheart." He hugged her close. "I'm scared, too, but you know what? The storm will stop soon and everything will be fine."

"Will it, Jack?" Avery asked. "What do *you* know about the weather here? Don't make her more promises you can't keep."

"What the hell is the matter with you?" he retorted, covering Mara's ears. "Are you *trying* to terrify her?"

"We wouldn't be here if not for you, Jack!" She paused and visibly struggled to calm down and breathe. "Did you even hear what your daughter said?"

Afraid she would see how deeply her words—and Mara's—had wounded him, Jack fled with Mara to the piloting station. Once inside, he sealed the hatch and diverted all nonessential power to the security sphere. He also programmed the system to scan the storm to aid in future weather forecasts. He might not know a thing about the weather on Vyndrae—Avery was right about that—but it was not too late to learn; he was realizing that was true about so many things.

Mara buried her head in his shoulder and continued to cry, though he thought it due more to tiredness now than fear. He carried her to the section where the pilot would typically rest, and gently put her down and tucked her in. He sat beside her on the small bed and leaned against the wall. There would be time to talk to her in the morning. He needed her to understand how sorry he was that his actions—*his selfishness*—had forced them to have to flee their home.

~

Hail battered the hull, waking Jack to the red glow of the auxiliary lights. The sound told him that the security sphere had failed, and the red lights let him know primary power was out as well. But something else entirely made him bolt upright: Mara was no longer sleeping curled by his side.

"Mara?"

No answer came. He repeated the increasingly frantic call until Avery joined him in the corridor outside the piloting station door.

"What's going on?" she asked, tired eyes lined with worry.

"I can't find Mara."

A moment of silence followed, in which he heard the wind whistling nearby, before Avery shouted, "What do you mean...*you can't find her?*"

Thunder jarred the ship, its rumble louder than it should have been. It hit him then—the reason it sounded so loud and the reason he had heard the cry of the wind so clearly before.

"The hatch!" He pushed past Avery and charged down the corridor. She hurried after him, gasping for air.

The mantle of gray mist had separated from the waves and merged with the thick ceiling of clouds, darkening to match their terrible blackness. The union created a smoky miasma, as if behind it all the very heavens were aflame. Jack lowered his head and pushed through the whirling sand and hail, the fury of the storm slinging both at him with enough force to raise welts.

"Mara!"

Her voice carried on the wind, tiny—like the mewing of a kitten—beneath the raging of the storm. "Papa!"

"It came from the direction of the treehouse," Avery said. She hurled each word at him like a dagger, tip poisoned with accusation.

He dashed for the treehouse without responding, rocks and roots biting into his hands and knees as he stumbled and clawed his way up the incline. When he reached the top, he clutched a handful of muddy moss and hauled himself over the edge. Blood dripped into his eyes from a slice across his forehead, but still he saw Mara dangling off the edge of the treehouse, the tattered strip of cloth gripped in her little hand. Only the density of the treetops kept the storm from snatching her away right there before his very eyes.

But Jack could see her hands slipping. All else faded. "Just hang on, sweetheart! Papa is com—"

Her red hair lifted. That was what he noticed first. That was what stole his voice. That was what he would never forget. *Her red hair lifted.*

~

Jack buried Mara with her doll. Having it in her arms made her appear asleep, reality a far more harrowing truth—as it so often proved to be.

He jabbed a stick into the soft soil of her grave and tied the dingy strip of white cloth around it. She had wanted the blasted thing so badly that he did not have the heart to keep it from her now, in spite of how terribly it pained him to see it there fluttering in the wind. She climbed the treehouse after it, sacrificed everything for it. Perhaps she had hoped to use it to wipe away the storm...

Avery approached, red hair tangled, face swollen from crying. "You take that down," she snarled, "or I will slit your throat while you sleep." She spoke with just enough conviction that it disturbed him.

"I wanted her to—"

"Get rid of it!"

"Mara earned that piece of cloth, *she died for it,* and I'm not taking it from her. If you want it gone, *you* get rid of it."

"How can you live with yourself, you miserable bastard?"

"I lost her, too, Avery."

"No, *Jack,* you killed her."

"That's not fair," he said. But it was. He knew it was.

There was nothing left to say, nothing left between them but grief and anger and a daughter's ghost. He turned and hurried to the shelter, which he had finished while Avery barricaded herself in the ship for two days with Mara's body. He just stood inside without purpose, without thought. It seemed too late to do anything worth doing.

Grief and remorse devoured him, leaving untouched only the exhausted, diseased parts of him. If only he had done everything necessary on Detra to keep Mara safe, but even the threat of hard time had frightened him. He slumped against the wall and buried his face in his hands. The time he was serving now—without her—was much worse than what the Zetrians would have had him serve. Much worse.

He should have been a better papa, instead of such an ignorant fool. He should have been a better husband, instead of such a self-absorbed coward. He should have been *faster*.

~

Sunlight exposed the many gaps in the crudely built shelter. A rumbling—which must have roused him—muffled the swish of waves caressing the sand.

Jack stood and staggered toward the door—those ravenous thoughts had filled his dreams with blood and blackness, remnants of which still coated him like a suffocating caul. He stepped out onto the beach just in time to watch the clouds swallow the glint of morning off a ship...*their* ship. A supply crate sat in the clearing where they had landed two weeks prior and a stick with a dingy strip of white cloth fluttered there atop it.

That told him everything he needed to know. And of all the things he had feared would happen, Avery marooning him had not been one of them. The possibility had never crossed his mind, though now that it had happened it felt as if it had been inevitable.

"Of course she would, you self-absorbed coward," he said. The rumbling abated, quickly replaced with the clap of lightning, which he thought looked more the color of spilled blood than that of an Enceladus plume. All of it reminded him of death now. Everything.

He could not afford to care that Avery had left, nor about what was in the crate; it did not matter. There was only room to care about one thing, and that was correcting the blunder he had made, the one he could correct: the treehouse. He would destroy it, just as Avery had asked one day before Mara fell—*one day before*. If only he had listened.

Grief drove him to follow his own footsteps from that awful night, like a drunk finding his way home. But once he was inside the treehouse, he could not tear his gaze away from the wall. There, drawn by a poignantly familiar hand, was the chalky outline of a doll. Above the drawing, Mara had scrawled several puffs of clouds, jagged bolts of lightning alongside.

"I drew her on the wall first, because the treehouse told me to, and then *I found her. I think this is magic chalk."*

Her voice pummeled him, spurring him outside and down to the forest floor. He finally understood the trees, and they all spoke with Mara's voice. He closed his eyes tight and heard a thousand of them repeating her words. Once he had absorbed all he could handle, had filled his mind beyond capacity, he opened his eyes...

...and found himself kneeling on the beach in the exact spot where he had snatched Mara into his arms and fled the looming storm. It had happened moments after she had shown him the chalk. *There it was*, protruding from the sand where she had dropped it: Mara's magic piece of chalk.

He held it as carefully as one would a delicate flower and retraced his steps back to the base of the treehouse. The trees closed in, their creaks morphing from singing to laughter. He ignored them and climbed inside. Mara's voice, or perhaps it was that of the treehouse—Mara *had* claimed it talked to her—stopped its urging.

Regardless of whether her ghost had led him to the chalk, or if the urging of the treehouse had, or even if his own frayed mind had, Jack knew what to do next. He could not, *would not*, go on without Mara. He knelt where he imagined she had sat and drawn her doll, adding the terrible storm in hopes they could watch the rain together again. He drew his happy, *living* Mara running in the white sand barefoot with clear skies and calm waters all around.

The same urge that had led him to the chalk now compelled him back to the beach. He sat in the wet sand and faced the supply crate, his chalky hands clenched in his lap and turning his thighs white. The dingy cloth remained there atop the crate, a reminder of all he had lost, a symbol of all he hoped to regain.

Jack pulled his thoughts inward and waited for his little girl, doing his best not to think about filthy dolls and black storms.

David G. Blake lives in an undisclosed location and spends his time trying to hack NASA's control systems so he can take Curiosity for a spin around Mars. In addition to *Shock Totem*, his work is forthcoming or has appeared in *Galaxy's Edge*, *Fantastic Stories of the Imagination*, *Nature*, *Beneath Ceaseless Skies*, and many other publications.

For more info, visit www.facebook.com/dgblake.

Howling Through the Keyhole

The stories behind the stories.

"The Henson Curse"

I was walking into a grocery store on a summer evening. The store had these somewhat mysterious fans, mounted just inside the doorway, blowing air more or less straight down. As I entered, the fans rustled the hair on my arms. To what purpose these fans, I couldn't begin to guess, and I thought *That's weird.* Immediately followed by the related thought: *And it would be even weirder if I had purple fur.*

These are the kind of lunatic thoughts that occur to me, usually without context or precedent. Maybe other people do this, too, I don't know. The vast majority of these thoughts are just nonsensical; useless, instantly discarded mind fluff. I barely even notice how weird I am behind the filter (some might suggest I'm pretty weird in front of the filter, too; I'd not be surprised to find a significant amount of this is trickling through). But occasionally one or two of these screwball musings will warrant additional consideration.

In this case purple fur led to some free-association and Muppets sprang readily to mind. I imagined someone walking into a supermarket with a Muppet on their hand, the brightly-colored fur agitated in the breeze of a doorway fan. That was really all I had to go on, but where it kind of crystalized was with the question, "Why would someone bring a puppet into a store?" The answer was, I guess, "Because

they couldn't take it off."

The mechanism behind that answer became the core of the story's idea. The rest of it was a long sequence of asking myself what a world looks like with a sudden and possibly mystical new tragic minority.

I had some distant familiarity with puppeteers. A couple of my childhood friends are professional puppet-makers and operators. Some research had to be done on the life and passing of Jim Henson; it was only fortune that allowed the twenty-fifth anniversary of his rather abrupt and tragic death to fall into the very near future as I wrote (sometime in 2013). It seemed like an appropriately creepy time to set my Awakening event into motion.

A special thanks is owed my wife, Nikki, for the creation of this story. She was an early fan and champion of it, suffered through numerous redrafts and rewrites, and demanded that it not be abandoned even when it seemed too difficult to bring Junjun and Zack's story to a readable state.

This one is for her.

–Paul A. Hamilton

"Blue John"

The first draft of "Blue John" included a demon-possessed letterpress that compelled Blue John to murder. Which, of course, meant Blue John was simply a conduit for evil and a rather one-dimensional character. After reading *The Invention of Murder*, a non-fiction book by Judith Flanders about the treatment of crime in the Victorian era press, I realized Blue John had plenty of motivation to kill and didn't need any satanic prompting. As Blue John became more real to me, so did the character of Finch—and he ended up taking over the story.

–*D.K. Wayrd*

"Three Years Ago This May"

I like to read fiction that punches me in the gut. To steal a term from my scotch-drinking friends, I prefer stories with a strong "finish."

One of the most effective finishes I've ever read was Jack Ketchum's "The Box." When I closed that story my jaw was on the floor. I felt as if someone had kicked me in the balls and then stole my wallet. It stuck with me for a long time, longer than any other story I can remember. While "The Box" is still the most effective finish I've experienced, it wasn't my first. That came decades earlier courtesy of Edwin Arlington Robinson's poem "Richard Cory."

"Three Years Ago This May" was my attempt to write a short story with a strong finish. I'm sure that subconsciously I was channeling both Ketchum and Robinson, but there was something else going on there too. I wanted to explore the all-to-familiar idea of being unable to live without the one(s) we love. We've all thought about it. Some of us have probably said it, but how many of us actually meant it? My nameless narrator… She meant it.

I hope you enjoyed the story. And I'll be honest; I hope it kicked you in the balls. You can keep your wallet.

–*Trace Conger*

"Malediction"

"Malediction" is a story based on sleep paralysis. I guess things that are bad for other people are good for writers, because thanks to sleep paralysis I've seen devils and angels and demons and spirits and the reaper, all while technically awake but paralyzed and hallucinating. One night, as I slept in a squatted house (taken from an imprisoned Dutch mafia boss, not a dead woman in Baltimore), one of these angels (I won't tell you which one) came and kissed me and bestowed its curse. This happened a decade back, and I think about it far too often. Eventually, I told this story to Catherine Grant, and she challenged me to turn it into fiction. A few false starts later, I wrote "Malediction."

–*Margaret Killjoy*

"Sweet William"

When you grow up on a farm, you see a lot of plants and animals. You see so many that inevitably you're going to run into some cases where things have gone *wrong*. A calf born without eyes, a piglet with a malformed limb, and plants with thick, fused stalks, as though ten or twenty plants have all been melted into one grotesque whole. Opening an ear of corn to find a blue-black mass of mold inside.

I managed to come to terms with the calf and the piglet—they were sweet-tempered animals—but the freaky plants scared the ever-loving crap out of me. I hacked them to bits with a shovel whenever I found them, because the only other alternative was never leaving the house again, but the uneasy, uncanny feeling the sight of them created in me lingered long after I shut my eyes at night.

"Sweet William" is my best attempt to share that unsettling feeling with readers. I don't know if it's just me, or whether other people (even other farm kids) just aren't looking, but my friends never seem to notice the things that grow *wrong* until I start to point them out.

Don't take my word on it. Look for yourself. Go for a walk in the spring and take a close look at all the dandelions you pass. Sooner or later, you're going to find one that's...not quite right. Maybe more than one. Maybe...maybe...too many.

—Mary Pletsch

"Deerborn"

Growing up in the suburbs, I was always amazed at how much effort was spent trying to keep nature—the wild, unruly aspects of nature, out. Of course that effort, like the effort to control and monitor the suburb's teenagers, was futile. There is always something growing stronger, pressing against barriers, and sneaking through.

—Leslie J. Anderson

"There's a Tongue in the Drain"

I wrote "There's a Tongue in the Drain" in response to the Shock Totem September Flash Fiction Contest. The prompt was a photograph of a drain with a shoe next to it. It was a nice shoe. I'm assuming there was once a foot in it, but you never know.

I'm a very visual person, and I could see a tongue poking through the grate and licking that shoe. My mom's voice rang down from thirty years past: "Wipe your feet. I just cleaned this floor!"

From that point on the story wrote itself. I like bent fairy tales and domestic situations. I wanted to incorporate the giant in the home like central air conditioning or a gas range. It was good fun writing it, and I'm happy with the result.

—Roger Lovelace

"Wasps"

When I was a Girl Scout (yes, really) I wandered down to the creek on one of our camping trips. I saw what I thought was a snakeskin and picked it up. Well, it wasn't a snakeskin; it was a wasp nest that had been knocked from a tree and trampled flat. I didn't have this revelation in time, however. My memory is a demented blur of buzzing, pain and terror. I never wanted to revisit it, but since we all unearth our horrors when we write this kind of stuff, I decided to finally put the episode in a story. I was fortunate enough to be on the ground when I was attacked; my dad is the one who had the experience in the tree. He told me he had no choice but to let them keep stinging him as he made his slow way down to the bottom and the horror of that has always stayed with me.

Mitzie is mostly fiction. She's a Frankensteinian blend of various childhood friends. I'm fascinated by the weird and passionate dynamic in girl friendships at that age, and particularly by the ghosts of our past. Events that shape and haunt us.

The blood-sisters bit actually happened but that girl was very sweet and nothing at all like the bullying Mitzie. Domino was real too, as was the long walk to identify his body. My dad was with me at the time and I ran away crying, so I guess he had to bring the body home for us to bury. (Our backyard was a vast pet cemetery, teeming with dogs, cats, rabbits, birds, lizards, snakes, mice, rats and guinea pigs. I have to wonder if the people who bought the house later found all those bones.)

What else? Oh yes, the funhouse. My sister and I used to play with these kids who lived down the street and there was an old cabin in their backyard where their grandfather had once lived. We used to love playing in that derelict place and we tried to turn it into a proper haunted house, rigging up scares for each other. I bet kids today never get the chance to play somewhere like that!

– *Thana Niveau*

"The Tall Man"

At risk of my backstory running longer than the microfiction tale itself, I'll keep this brief, though I could speak for days on "brainstorming."

If I'm not working on any specific project, I'll try freeing my mind and just jot down whatever haphazard thoughts or caffeinated ideas I can imagine, spending no more than one or two sentences on each. Usually most of it is dreck, but without fail there's always something that particularly piques my interest, and I start writing about it. Sometimes the writing goes nowhere. In this case, my childhood fascination with the Guinness Book of World Records inspired me to add a supernatural twist to a record. Originally the story was much longer; I wrote it in one night and then it took me a week to reduce it to two hundred words!

– *Eric J. Guignard*

"Winter Fever"

Sometime around Christmas 2013, I caught a fever. It was bad, the kind that left me stuffed inside my bed, weak and sweating, as dreams tore off strips of my lucidity one repetitious nightmare at a time. I don't remember exactly what the nightmares were about, but I have fuzzy memories of similar ones I've had before: screaming logs rolling down a hillside toward a secluded cabin in the woods, or mumbling politicians slithering over each other's bodies like a pit full of snakes.

That winter Oregon experienced a heavy snowfall, which buried our town in knee-deep powder-white. On the occasions I glanced out the window, the only signs of life were the black streaks of tire tracks cutting through the streets. Never people, pets or even wild animals. It looked like the town had been abandoned and, in my altered state of mind, I felt lonely surveying all that emptiness from the confines of my darkened bedroom.

Some months later, that experience became the backbone of "Winter Fever." The first scene came to me immediately. In my mind, I saw a man shoveling his walkway on some lonely country acre. He felt isolated among the flat and barren fields surrounding him, but he was anything but alone. It took a bit of work discovering the nature of his antagonist. I knew it would manifest as a little girl because the way children think often reminds me of the illogic—and even madness—of fever dreams. In a few hours, I had a working draft and, a few months after that, I managed to nail all the disparate pieces into place.

–Samuel Marzioli

"The Eavesdropper"

The good guys have stories, but so do the monsters, and often they aren't that different. Perspective is everything, after all. Monsters do tend to be brief, however, because while they enjoy telling their stories, what they're best at is listening to ours.

–Sarah L. Johnson

"The Last Treehouse"

In February 2013, my story "To My Father" (*Nature*, Volume 493, Issue 7434) was named Shock Totem's Short Story of the Week. In a later discussion regarding that selection, Ken mentioned to me that he had always wanted to publish a science fiction/horror hybrid in *Shock Totem*. I tried a few hybrids soon after that conversation, but they all came out as flash, and I wanted something longer to send him.

The idea of Vyndrae came first. A secluded planet, abandoned and lost. The ideal hiding spot for a man on the run. I wrote the first couple scenes with just that in mind. When I finished those and started working on what would come next for Jack and his family, I discovered the tragedy in store for them and knew that "The Last Treehouse" was the perfect story for the hybrid I had been wanting to write for well over a year. I could not be more pleased and appreciative that Ken and John agreed.

–David G. Blake

SILENT Q DESIGN

Silent Q Design was founded in Montreal in 2006 by **Mikio Murakami.** Melding together the use of both realistic templates and surreal imagery, Mikio's artistry proves, at first glance, that a passion for art still is alive, and that no musician, magazine, or venue should suffer from the same bland designs that have been re-hashed over and over.

Mikio's work has been commissioned both locally and internationally, by bands such as **Redemption, Synastry, Starkweather,** and **Epocholypse.** *Shock Totem #3* was his first book design project.

For more info, visit **www.silentqdesign.net.**

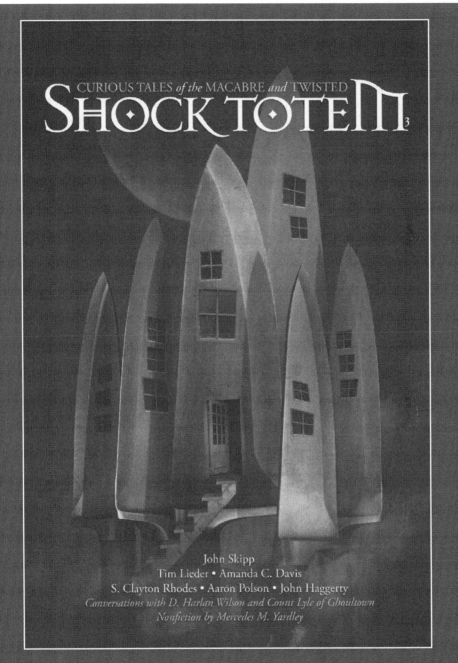

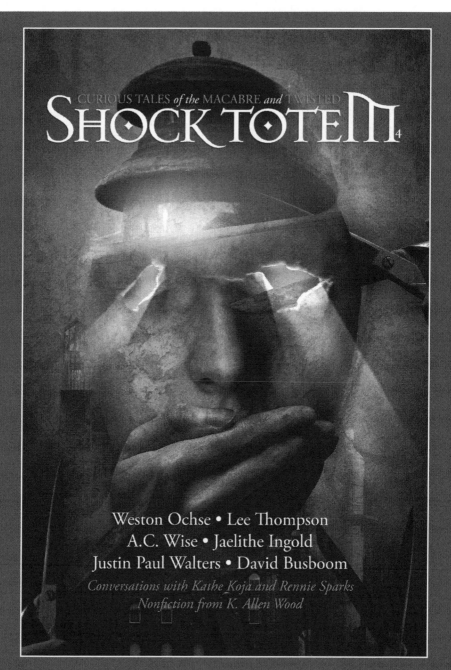

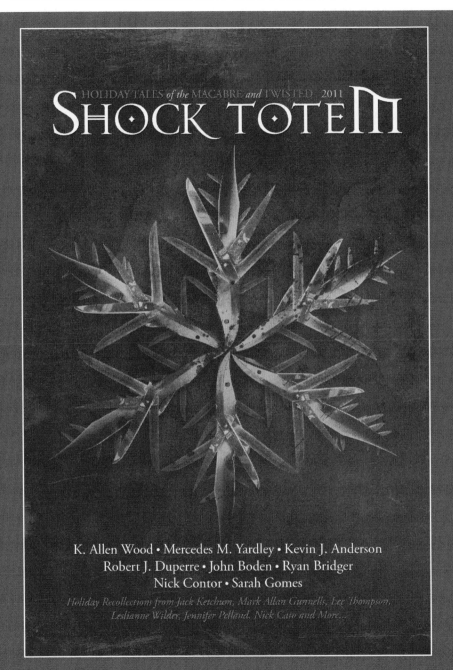

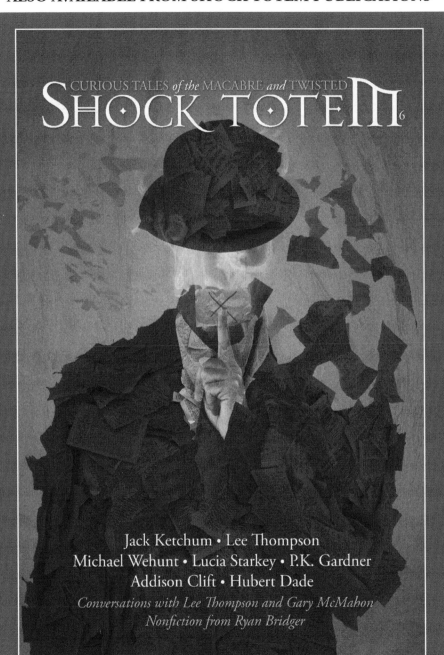

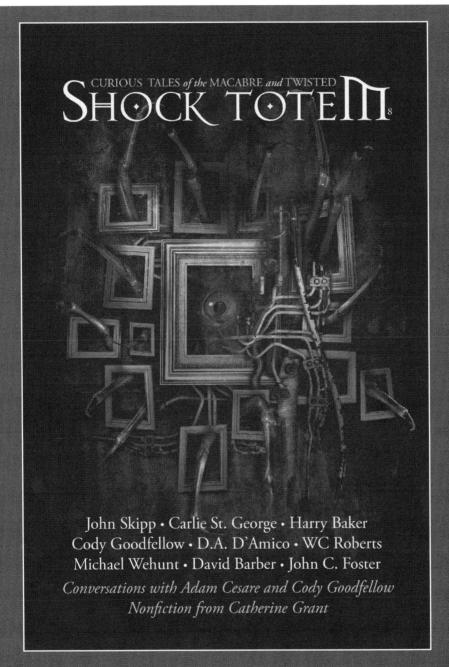

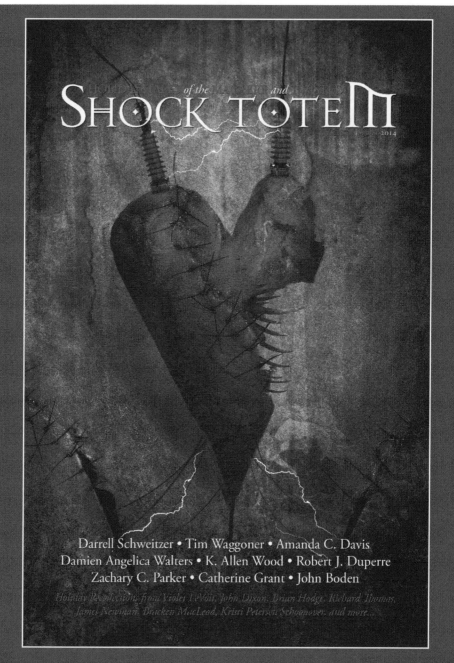

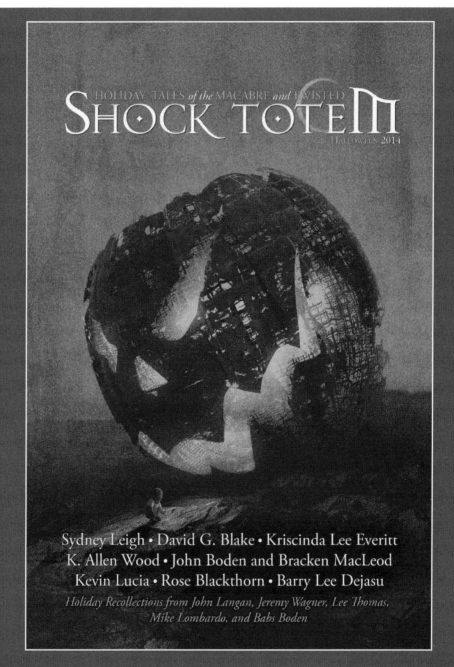

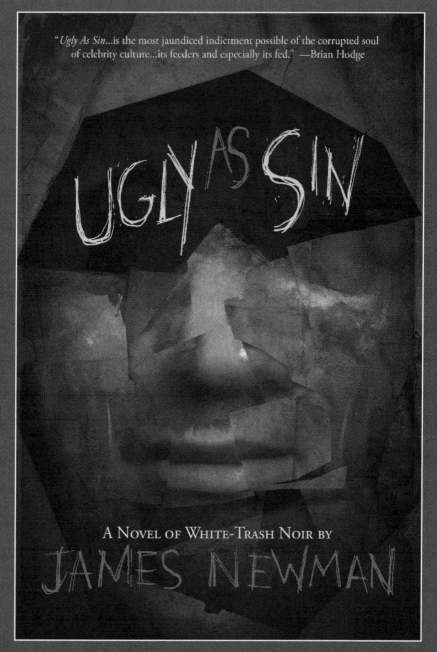

Find Us Online

http://www.shocktotem.com
http://www.twitter.com/shocktotem
http://www.facebook.com/shocktotem
http://www.youtube.com/shocktotemmag

Servant Leadership

A Biblical Study for Becoming a Christlike Leader

"A Woman's Guide" series
—Revised Edition

Rhonda H. Kelley

NEW HOPE
PUBLISHERS
Birmingham, Alabama

New Hope Publishers
P. O. Box 12065
Birmingham, AL 35202-2065
www.newhopepublishers.com

Library of Congress Cataloging-in-Publication Data

Kelley, Rhonda.
  Servant leadership : a woman's guide : a biblical study for becoming a Christlike leader / Rhonda H. Kelley.
      p. cm.
  Includes bibliographical references and index.
  ISBN-13: 978-1-59669-258-9 (sc : alk. paper)
  ISBN-10: 1-59669-258-8 (sc : alk. paper)
  1. Christian leadership--Biblical teaching. 2. Christian leadership--Textbooks. 3. Women in church work--Textbooks. 4. Leadership in women--Textbooks. I. Title.
  BV652.K45 2011
  253.082--dc22
                        2011009406

ISBN-10: 1-59669-258-8
ISBN-13: 978-1-59669-258-9
N104129 • 0611 • 2M1